Foreword

Although people have schlepped greywater aro
immemorial, the modern generation of systems, whi
mated and efficient delivery, have been in use only a few years.

Legal methods of greywater use tend to employ engineering overkill while most of the simple and economical methods (those which people actually use) remain technically illegal. Due to the legality issue and the unproven nature of most systems, government agencies and contractors are reluctant to speak frankly about them (if indeed they knew anything about them). This information void leaves hundreds of thousands of do-it-yourselfers to "reinvent the wheel" with little useful guidance. This book aims to fill that void.

This revised new edition includes several pages of new information, much of it inspired by consulting in Northern California and Central America. It also accounts for the recent greywater revolution in the South West.[2] The Southern California-centric coverage seven revisions ago is now more international, though it still speaks most directly to first-world design conditions.

This edition, with four times the information contained in the first, presents principles to use as a guide for breaking new ground, as well as an expanded range of proven designs, both legal and illegal, ancient and experimental.

Art Ludwig
San Jose Creek, Santa Barbara, California

Contents

The competition: a seawater desalination plant (above) provides some of the world's most costly fresh water.

An activated sludge sewage treatment plant (below) dumps greywater in the ocean after energy and chemical intensive treatment.

Introduction

On Christmas eve of the year I turned 15, my present to the family was to move out into a decaying tack room in the lower reaches of our backyard. The tack room plumbing consisted of a lone hose bib in front of the porch. If I could deal with a lack of plumbing while backpacking, I reasoned, I should be able to figure this out. The eco-cidal adult establishment thought it needed all of that over-engineered infrastructure, but I surely didn't.

BATHING GARDEN

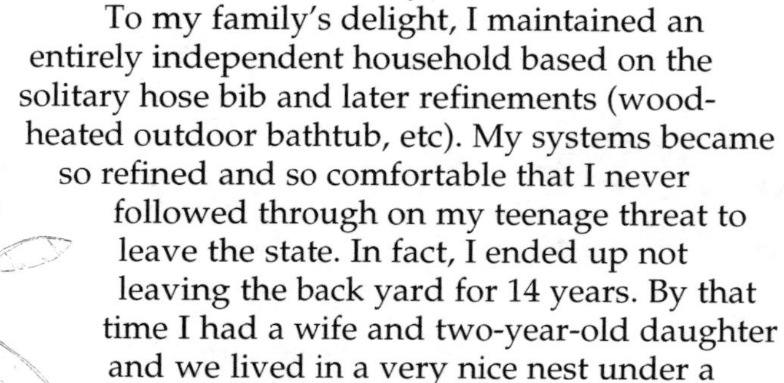

To my family's delight, I maintained an entirely independent household based on the solitary hose bib and later refinements (wood-heated outdoor bathtub, etc). My systems became so refined and so comfortable that I never followed through on my teenage threat to leave the state. In fact, I ended up not leaving the back yard for 14 years. By that time I had a wife and two-year-old daughter and we lived in a very nice nest under a pepper tree, as my business had taken over the tack room.

There were a few breaks during my extended stay. Once I bicycled around the world for three years, witnessing myriad philosophies of wastewater management. Another time, I left to study ecological design at U.C. Berkeley. My thesis was that *every house could be surrounded with an oasis of biological productivity nourished by the flow of nutrients and water from the home.* This seemed natural, as most of the elements added to water in the home are plant nutrients. If only the small amount of toxins in cleaning agents could be eliminated, nutrients and water from the home could nurture its edible landscaping on a sustainable basis.

However, I found that cleaners bio*compatible* with plants or soil were not available. In fact, there was little evidence that the idea had been pursued at all. In my research, I had learned enough and befriended enough experts to assemble a team to create biocompatible cleaners to my own specifications.

About this time, my home town of Santa Barbara, in an advanced stage of drying up and blowing away due to prolonged drought, became the first in the nation to legalize greywater use for irrigation. Consequently, I took a six-year side trip from my ecological design work to develop, produce and market Oasis Biocompatible Cleaners. I sold this business in 1996,[s15] and have been consulting, writing and gardening since then. The Oasis greywater books, which started as a pamphlet to save us time answering questions, are now the main part of my business.

During these past several years, I've walked a narrow strip of neutral ground between warring factions during a period of sweeping changes in the emergent greywater industry. Our customers entrust us with their darkest greywater secrets, system manufacturers keep us abreast of their offerings and experiences, academics appreciate our research and, unsullied by the actual stain of greywater on our commercial hands, we enjoy unprejudiced reception by regulators. This edition incorporates knowledge gleaned during this time, as well as recent experience from consulting internationally and a few of my own original designs.

What is Greywater?

Any wastewater used in the home, except water from toilets, is called *greywater.* Dish, shower, sink and laundry water comprise 50-80% of residential "wastewater." This may be reused for other purposes, especially landscape irrigation. Toilet-flush water is called *blackwater.* A few systems which can safely recycle toilet water are included in this book. Contaminated or difficult to handle greywater, such as solids laden kitchen sink water or water used to launder diapers, I call "*dark* grey" water; some regulators consider these blackwater. Wastewater without added solids, such warm-up water from the hot water faucet, reverse-osmosis reject water or refrigera compressor drip water, is called *clearwater*. *Reclaimed water* (highly treated municipa greywater and blackwater, usually piped to large-volume users such as golf course in a separate distribution system) is outside the scope of this book.

Why Use Greywater?

It's a waste to irrigate with great quantities of drinking water when plants thrive on used water containing small bits of compost. Unlike many ecological stopgap measures, greywater use is a part of the fundamental solution to many ecological problems and will probably remain essentially unchanged in the distant future. The benefits of greywater recycling include:

Lower fresh water use

Greywater can replace fresh water in many instances, saving money and incre ing the effective water supply in regions where irrigation is needed. Residential wa use is almost evenly split between indoor and outdoor. All except toilet water coul be recycled outdoors, achieving the same result with significantly less water divert from nature.

Less strain on septic tank or treatment plant

Greywater use greatly extends the useful life and capacity of septic systems. F municipal treatment systems, decreased wastewater flow means higher treatment effectiveness and lower costs.

Greywater reuse follows the same principles that make wild rivers clean even though they drain square miles of dirt, worms and feces. Beneficial bacteria break down nasties into water-soluble plant food, and the plants eat it, leaving pure water. The author is shown here deeply absorbed in his tireless study of this process.

Highly effective purification

Greywater is purified to a spectacularly high degree in the upper, most biologically active region of the soil.[1] This protects the quality of natural surface an ground waters.

Site unsuitable for a septic tank

For sites with slow soil percolation or other problems, a greywater system can a partial or complete substitute for a very costly, over-engineered system.

Less energy and chemical use

Less energy and chemicals are used due to the reduced amount of both freshwater and wastewater that needs pumping and treatment. For those providing thei own water or electricity, the advantage of a reduced burden on the infrastructure is felt directly. Also, treating your wastewater in the soil under your own fruit trees definitely encourages you to dump fewer toxic chemicals down the drain.

Groundwater recharge

Greywater application in excess of plant needs recharges groundwater.

Plant growth

Greywater enables a landscape to flourish where water may not otherwise be available to support much plant growth.

Reclamation of otherwise wasted nutrients

Loss of nutrients through wastewater disposal in rivers or oceans is a subtle, b highly significant form of erosion. Reclaiming nutrients in greywater helps to maintain the fertility of the land.

Increased awareness of and sensitivity to natural cycles

Greywater use yields the satisfaction of taking responsibility for the wise husbandry of an important resource.

Just because

Greywater is relatively harmless and great fun to experiment with. Moreover, life with alternative waste treatment can be less expensive and more interesting.

When Not to Use Greywater

There are a number of possible reasons not to use greywater or to use it only during certain times of year:

Insufficient space

In some situations, neighbors are too close, the yard too small or nonexistent.

Drain pipes impossible to get to

If all plumbing is entombed under a concrete slab, accessing most of the greywater won't be economical.

Unsuitable soil

Soil that is extremely permeable or impermeable may preclude the use of a greywater system or at least require special adaptations.

Unsuitable climate

In very wet climates, where using greywater for irrigation is of little benefit, better ways to dispose of it may be available. In very cold climates (see page 34), freezing may prevent the use of a greywater system for part of the year.

Insufficient combined waste flow

If all greywater is reused, the flow through municipal sewers designed for higher flow may occasionally be insufficient to move toilet solids through.

Legality concerns

In most of the developed world, the legality of greywater systems is a "grey" area. However, there seems to be a movement toward a less paranoid, more realistic official attitude regarding greywater recycling, concurrent with increased experience and improved systems (not to mention water shortages and pollution problems).[2] For example, all the systems described here are newly legal in Arizona and New Mexico.

Authorities generally turn a blind eye toward greywater use even where illegal. California, for example, once published a pamphlet that explained the illegality of greywater use then explained how to do it—and get a tax credit for it!

Health concerns

The reason cited for keeping greywater illegal in many areas is concern for public health. In practice, the health threat from greywater has proven to be insignificant. I know of no documented instance in which a person in the U.S. became ill from greywater. A quantitative field test by the Department of Water Reclamation in Los Angeles found that greywatered soil did teem with pathogens. However, the control soil did too! Their conclusion: don't eat dirt, with or without greywater.[3]

Poor cost/benefit ratio

In some situations, especially when legal requirements mandate a complex system for a small flow of water, the ecological cost of the system may outweigh the benefits.

Inconvenience

So far, many greywater systems are either more expensive or require considerably more user involvement than well-functioning septic or sewer systems.

Health Considerations Concerning Greywater Use

Greywater may contain infectious organisms, so keep this in mind when designing and using a system. In practice, the health risk of greywater use has proven to be minimal. It is, after all, the water you just bathed in, or residue from clothes you wore not long ago. At the same time, it's definitely poor form to construct pathways for infecting people into your design, and totally unnecessary. Al greywater safety guidelines stem from these two principles:

1) Greywater must pass slowly through healthy topsoil for natural purification to occur.

2) Design your greywater system so no contact takes place before purification.

Beautifully made but ill-conceived greywater storage tank. This four foot wide, four foot deep tank is the final of a four-chamber system which converts greywater to foul-smelling blackwater over the course of the week it takes to get through the system. The water is dark black, smells vicious, and generates hydrogen sulfide which has eaten through the steel lid.

Here are examples of applying these principles to correct possible problems:

- ***Direct contact or consumption.*** SOLUTION: carefully avoid cross connections a label greywater plumbing, including greywater garden hoses. Use gloves wh cleaning greywater filters. Wash your hands after contact with greywater.
- ***Microorganisms on plants.*** Direct application to foliage can leave untreated microorganisms on surfaces. SOLUTION: don't apply greywater to lawns (see *A Note on Lawns*, page 8) or fruits and vegetables that are eaten raw (strawberries, lettuce, or carrots, for example). Watering fruit trees is acceptable if greywater is applied under mulch.
- ***System overload.*** Greywater systems are safest when using water that is fairl clean initially. Greywater should not contain water used to launder soiled diapers or used by anyone with an infectious disease; in both cases, greywate should be diverted to the septic tank or sewer. Also, DON'T STORE GREYWATER; use it within 24 hours, before bacteria multiply. Finally, if you are having a party where 50 people are going to use a system designed for two, consider diverting greywater to the sewer for the night.
- ***Breathing of microorganisms.*** Droplets from sprinklers can evaporate to leav harmful microorganisms suspended in the air, waiting for someone to breathe them. SOLUTION: don't recycle greywater through sprinklers.
- ***Contamination of surface water.*** If greywater does not percolate through the soil, it can flow into creeks or other waterways untreated. SOLUTION: discharg greywater underground or into a mulch-filled basin. Don't apply greywater t saturated soils. Apply greywater intermittently so that it soaks in and soil ca aerate between waterings. In general, greywater which is confined subsurfac or within mulch basins at least 50 feet from a creek or lake is not a problem.

Laundry water discharging onto the public street from a mansion in the hills above Los Angeles. Without soil, there is no purification.

- ***Chemical contamination.*** Biological purification does not usually remove industrial toxins. Toxins either will be absorbed by plants or will pollute groundwater. Many household cleaners are composed of chemicals that are unsuitable for introduction into a biological system (see page 24). SOLUTION: don't buy products that you wouldn't want in your greywater system. Divert water containing those you can't avoid to poison the sewer or septic instead.
- ***Contamination of groundwater.*** It is all but impossible to contaminate groun water with a greywater system (unless you live over a fissured limestone aquifer). However, those with wells probably should not apply greywater an closer to the well than county regulations allow a septic tank leachfield.

Editorial note on health risks

Much has been made over the *potential* health risk of greywater use, without comparison to *actual* risk from the common practice of sewage disposal in waters used for swimming, drinking and fishing. Approximately 20% of all U.S. communities dump sewage in natural waters after primary treatment (solids removal) only. This questionable practice short circuits natural purification in soil and is considered one of the least desirable by the World Health Organization.[4] During heavy rains, even the most technologically advanced treatment plants are forced to abandon all pretense of treatment and let raw sewage flood into the ocean or river.

Widespread greywater use in a population unaccustomed to taking responsibility for utilizing natural systems would not be risk-free. However, even with the inevitable misuses, greywater recycling as described here poses a low risk compared to other accepted activities (see page 42 and Appendix 6 of the *Builder's Greywater Guide* for much more on health considerations).

Greywater Sources

Homes without water conserving fixtures generate about 55 gallons of greywater per person per day. Conserving fixtures cut this to forty gallons (enough to water four mature fruit trees or a dozen shrubs). Extreme conservation habits can cut production to five gallons per day per person. Leaks can add 5% or more to water use.

You can use the table below as a guide to estimate the amount of greywater produced in your house. Group fixtures that share a common drain into subtotals (for example, bathroom sink, tub and shower often share the same drain).

TABLE 1: GREYWATER SOURCES AND QUALITIES

SOURCE/ *Ease of replumbing*	**QUALITY/** *Ways to improve quality*	**QUANTITY** *Average with-without conservation*
SOURCES WITH THEIR OWN PUMPS		
Washing Machine *Getting washer lint out of septic leachlines greatly extends their life. Easy do-it-yourself plumbing.*	**Good.** Medium concentration of soaps, lint. Diapers can dramatically increase pathogen level. *Can be improved to* ***excellent*** *by using biocompatible cleaners.*	**Large:** 30-50 gal per load (10 gal for front loader). 1.5 loads per week per adult, 2.5 per child. *85-100 gal/person/wk*
Automatic Dishwasher *May be easily replumbed by a do-it-yourselfer.*	**Poor.** Low to high quantity of solids depending upon degree of prerinsing. High salt and pH from conventional automatic dishwashing compounds; alternative cleaners don't clean well.	**Small:** 5-10 gal per load.
GRAVITYFLOWSOURCES		
Shower *Requires professional replumbing. May be impossible with slab foundation.*	**Excellent.** Minimal concentration of soap and shampoo is of little concern. Contains pump-snarling hair. *Use the least amount of soap and shampoo necessary. Use liquid soap.*	**Large:** average = 10 gal per day per person for low-flow shower; 20 for high-flow. *70-100 gal/person/wk*
Tub *Requires professional replumbing. May be impossible with slab foundation.*	**Excellent.** Same desirable qualities as shower, only more so.	**Large:** average = 40 gal per adult bath, 25 gal for kid's baths. *Use is highly variable*
Bathroom Sink *Requires professional replumbing.*	**Good.** Concentration of soap, shaving cream and toothpaste can be high. *Use liquid soap. Exercise discretion in choice and quantity of other products.*	**Small:** average = 1-5 gal per day per person.

(Continued on next page)

SOURCE/ *Ease of replumbing*	QUALITY/ *Ways to improve quality*	QUANTITY *Average with-without conservation*
GRAVITY FLOW SOURCES (CONT.)		
Kitchen Sink *Requires professional replumbing.*	**Good** but **Problematic** in delicate systems. High in nutrients, but also in solids, grease and soap. *Despite the relative absence of pathogens, many authorities consider kitchen sink water "blackwater" not worth trying to reuse. I like it, due to nutrient value, at least in vegetarian households with little grease in the water (meat eaters can add a grease trap). It can be a design problem for systems, but it is not a problem in the soil. One work around is to plumb only the rinse side of a double sink to the greywater system.*	**Medium:** 5-15 gal per day per person.
Reverse-Osmosis Water Purifier Wastewater *May be easily replumbed by a do-it-yourselfer.*	**Excellent.** "Clearwater"; usually no suspended solids. Contains 25% more concentration of the same dissolved solids as tap water.	**Medium:** 3-5 gal per gallon of drinking water used.
Water Softener Backwash *May be easily replumbed by a do-it-yourselfer.*	**Very bad.** Water softener backwash is extremely high in salt. *Use of potassium chloride salt*[s20] *instead of sodium chloride salt can raise its quality to* ***very poor,*** *but is still more of a disposal problem than a reuse opportunity.*	**Small:** 5% of indoor water use.
Softened Water	**Poor.** Softened water contains salt (sodium chloride), which is harmful for plants. *Potassium chloride*[s20] *can be used instead, raising its quality to* ***okay.*** *The best thing is to* ***disconnect the water softener.***	**All greywater** if softener is in use.
Toilet Water *Requires professional replumbing. May be impossible with slab foundation.*	**Very bad.** High concentration of potential pathogenic organisms, high suspended solids. Toilet water is blackwater inappropriate for reuse in an ordinary greywater system. *In a system designed to address the solids and health issues it poses, it would be* ***very good*** *(see constructed wetlands p. 23, sand filters p. 22)*	**Medium:** 5-8 gal per day per person low-flow; three times that for high-flow. *60-135 gal/person/wk*

Irrigation Requirements

On a sketch of your site, note the gallons per week available from each group of fixtures and the path of the plumbing. Then look at where in the yard they could go. For disposal, the only concern is to not overload the soil or sensitive plants (see **Design Loading Rates**, page 19). For reuse, note irrigation needs on the sketch. This is a complex and inexact science. Irrigation need can vary by a factor of ten from a foggy day to a day with hot dry wind. It is usually sufficient to figure an inch per week (that's 0.6 gallons per square foot of irrigated area per week). This will get you in the ball park (for more on calculating water needs, see the *Builder's Greywater Guide,* inside back cover). For trees, use the area under the canopy. You can adjust up or down for low water-need plants or extreme climates. Now consider how the greywater sources could be routed to areas of irrigation need, and how freshwater irrigation would be adjusted to actualize water savings.

Example of Wastewater Amounts
Two adults, two kids

Washer: 5 loads/week x 32 gal/load	= 160 gal/week
Shower: 1 shower/day/person x 8 min. x 2 gpm x 4 people x 7 days	= 448 gal/week
Tub: 2 baths/week x 30 gal	= 60 gal/week
Bathroom Sink: 2 gal/day/person x 4 people x 7 days	= 56 gal/week
Kitchen Sink: 3 gal/day/person x 4 people x 7 days	= 84 gal/week
Reverse Osmosis Water Purifier Wastewater (clearwater): ½ gal/day/person x 4 gal rejected/gal used x 4 people x 7 days	= 56 gal/week
Reusable Subtotal	= **864 gal/week**
Toilet: 3 flushes/day/person x 4 people x 7 days	= 126 gal/week
Total Indoor Water Use	= **990 gal/week**

Call it 1,000 gallons; this is 35 gallons per person per day indoors, below the 50 gpd average for households with piped in water, and above the 10 gpd average for households without.

Irrigation Needs
Quarter-acre lot

5 Large Fruit Trees	= 575 gal/week	Herb Garden	= 50 gal/week
7 Small Fruit Trees	= 100 gal/week	3 Veggie Beds	= 80 gal/week
533 ft^2 Fruiting Hedge	= 320 gal/week	15' x 20' Lawn	= 180gal/week
4 x 20' Wildflower Bed	= 10 gal/week	**Non-Greywaterable Subtotal**	= **310 gal/week**
Small Water Garden	= 30 gal/week		
Greywaterable Subtotal	= **1,035 gal/week**	**Grand Total**	= **1,345 gal/week**

This is 48 gallons per person per day outdoors, slightly below average.

Figure 1: Example—Matching Greywater Sources to Irrigation Needs

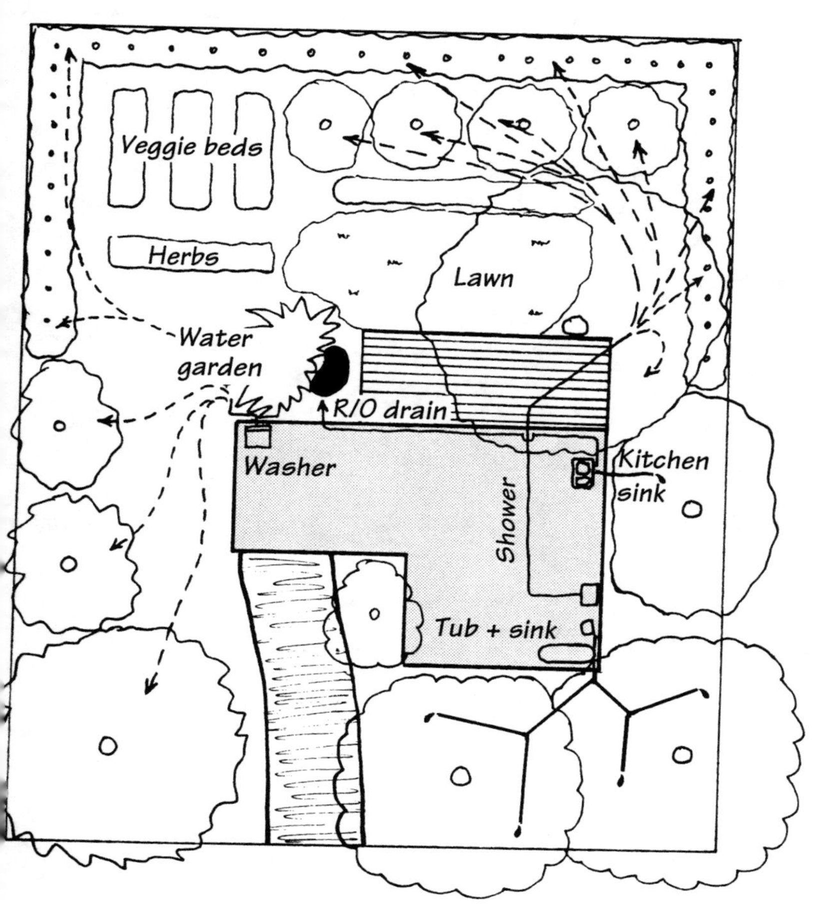

Greywater systems used:

Washer: "Drumless laundry system" to downhill and slight uphill plants.

Tub plus Bathroom Sink: "Branched drain to mulch basins" around large trees.

Shower: "Movable drain to mulch basins," plumbed to opposite side of house where irrigation need is greatest.

Kitchen Sink: "Drain to mulch basin" around one big tree.

Reverse Osmosis Water Purifier Wastewater (Clearwater): Through ½" drip irrigation tubing to water garden. *(Note: This small line would clog with greywater.)*

% Irrigation efficiency

The percentage of water actually used by plants is the irrigation efficiency. The rest evaporates from the soil or is lost below the roots. Drip irrigation can reach 80%, about the highest attainable. The average irrigation efficiency in the example above is 40%, so 864 gal/week of reused water will reduce freshwater irrigation by 350 gal/week or 25%.

Millionaire's lawn in a Los Angeles study. One side is irrigated with greywater through subsurface drip, the other with potable water; it's absolutely impossible to tell the difference. This system would be perfect for say, a high school with dozens of showers and acres of turf.

When people become accustomed to drip irrigation, they desire to make greywatering equally easy and efficient. The precise water distribution in a drip irrigation system is possible from relatively high pressure (20psi) in a line with small orifices. Greywater, in contrast, discharges from the house at zero pressure, full of orifice-clogging glop.

Automated, efficient distribution of greywater requires very fine filtering and pumping. Fine filters need to be cleaned frequently—every two weeks or so. Filter cleaning is a disgusting job, soon surrendered by all except the truly fanatical. It is possible to spend your way to a satisfactory engineering solution to the problem—for a few thousand dollars or more.

In the example on page 7, 40% greywatering efficiency means only a third to half of the total irrigation need will be met by greywater, far short of what is possible in theory. For most residences, the best approach is still to sacrifice automation and efficiency in favor of simplicity.

A note on lawns

The only acceptable way of irrigating lawns with greywater is with underground drip tubing[s2] supplied by a backwashing sand filter type system (pages 24, 43)—far beyond what most residences are likely to install. Unfortunately, turf accounts for the bulk of the irrigation need in the typical landscape, and lawn greywatering is a popular violation of common sense greywater safety rules.

We suggest that you replace most of your turf with something else and replace what's left with a water-conserving grass such as Tall Fescue. Water this with the freshwater you save from using greywater elsewhere, or just let your lawn go dormant when there's not enough rain to sustain it.

Choosing a Greywater System

Peruse the design considerations and system selection chart that follow. Consider each fixture set individually; it may be best to employ a few different systems, even in a small house. One of the systems will likely be adaptable to your situation as described. If not, the elements of each system can be rearranged to make a wide variety of other possible systems or serve as an inspirational starting-point for an as yet-unconceived variation. *Note that some designs are cautioned as being unproven.* Clearly, the risk is higher that you will waste time and money on something experimental, so proceed with caution. An incremental approach can reduce this risk. For example, one fixture set could be connected to a single "movable drain to mulch basins" hose. If everything worked well, the remaining fixtures could be connected and then a branched drain system added later.

For best results, choose the ***simplest possible*** *design and* ***build it as well as you possibly can.***

Greywater system design considerations

Objectives .... What are you trying to accomplish?
Irrigate?
Dispose of wastewater responsibly?
Other?

Regulatory climate .... Regulatory enforcement
Plumbing & building codes
Health codes
Applicable local, state and federal laws

Economics .... Ecological impact over project life cycle
Budget/payback requirements
Renter's construction
Resale value
Time and money for maintenance, replacement
Value of resources used & saved

Site characteristics .... Topography
Climate (temperature, rainfall, evaporation)
Soil type & perk rate (see note at left)
Possibility of a greenhouse (especially for cold, wet, low perk locations)
Availability of biocompatible cleaners
Nearby surface waters
Rain runoff pattern
Predictable disasters, e.g., flooding
Very high groundwater?
Existing and planned vegetation
Buildings & Property lines
Neighborhood appropriateness

System possibilities and requirements .. Existing treatment facilities
Water & GW sources (quantity, quality, surges, conservation measures to be implemented)
Optimum use of existing site features
Access to collection plumbing
Location of system components
Irrigation requirements
Match of system requirements to users
Availability of parts & skilled labor for construction, maintenance
Perfection standard, including hygiene standard

How to do a simple perk test

Dig holes to the depth the greywater will discharge (usually 6-12"), in the locations you wish to discharge it. Place stakes into the bottoms firmly. Mark reference levels and measure how many inches the water drops in a given number of minutes. Saturate the holes with water by filling 2-3 times. When the water drops the same amount a few time increments in a row, that's your measurement. Convert the numbers to percolation in minutes per inch, then see the table on page 19 for sizing your infiltration area. If it takes hours to drop an inch, or less than a minute, or if the hole fills with water by itself, you've got a problem!

What is perfection standard?

Do you want things 70% perfect? 90%? 95%? 98%? Perfection standards are a matter of cultural and personal preference. Each standard has its charm—and cost. This is a huge variable which is rarely discussed explicitly. Each of the above increments roughly doubles the amount of money, time and materials to do the job. In many cases it also doubles the negative environmental impact.

Note for new construction

Greywater use is best incorporated during the design phase. Like passive solar, it is a *primary* design consideration. It affects the location of the house and every other water feature on the land. The higher the greywater sources are above the irrigated area, the better. The more accessible the drain pipes, the better. *Elevation relationships between water features are critical and difficult to change once the house is built.* Don't let your plumber squander fall; make sure the pipes come out high as possible!

Legality is virtually never an issue for retrofits. Unless you live in Arizona or New Mexico, it is virtually *always* an issue for new construction or remodeling. This new dimension of difficulty is addressed in our *Builder's Greywater Guide* (see inside back cover). It may be desirable to arrange plumbing conventionally to pass inspection. Foresight will minimize effort and materials needed to incorporate greywater use later. With blackwater and greywater lines separate, installing a greywater system later will easy. Designing and building plumbing lines to work in septic/sewer as well as greywater modes will require the services of an especially skilled, cooperative plumber.

TABLE 2: SYSTEM SELECTION CHART

m=maybe 1=Most satisfactory
blank=no 5=Least satisfactory
y=yes
y=yes, very much so.

1=Easiest
5=Hardest

System Type	Overall grade when used in optimum application	Renter's Construction?	Can Irrigate Up-slope of Greywater Source?	Possible with Fixture Plumbing in Slab?	Suitable for 3rd world?	Proven?	Possibly Legal under UPC/CPC? (All are legal in AZ, NM)[2]	Ease of Construction	Ease of Use	Maintenance Required
Dishpan dump, Bucketing	**1**	y	y	y	y	y		1	5	
Garden hose through the bathroom	**3**	y		y	y	y		1	5	
Landscape direct	**1**	m			**y**	y	m	1-5	1	
Drain to mulch basin	**1**	m			**y**	y		2	1	
Branched drain to basins/leachfields	**1**				y	y, evolving	y	4	1	
Movable drain to mulch basins	**2**	m			m	y, evolving		2	3	
Gravity drum to mulch basins	**2**	y			y	y		2	3	
Drumless laundry to mulch basins	**2**	y	3ft		m	y, evolving		2	3	
Drum with pump, filter, hose	**4**	m	y			y, but mixed		3	4	
Drum with pump, filter, mini-leachfields or distribution cones	**4**		y			Yes, but mixed	y	4	4	
Infiltration beds (not a complete system; distribution field only)	**3**					y	y	4	3	
Leaching chamber, box trough (not a complete system; distribution field only)	**3**					y	y	3	2	
Multi-mode greywater tank	**1**		m[d]		y	New design		4	1-5[d]	
Plants over septic tank leachfield	**3**			y	y	Mixed	y	1	2	
Septic tank and "infiltrators"	**2**			y		New design	y	4	1	
Septic tank, sand filtration (not a complete system; treatment only)	**2**		y	y		Yes, still evolving	y	5	2	
Greywater greenhouse w/drum & pump to infiltration bed (or split drain to box trough)	**1**		m			Yes but evolving	y	5	2	
Constructed wetlands (NOTE: there may still be treated water to get rid of)	**2**			y	m	Yes, still evolving	y	5	2	
Automated systems	**1**		y		m	Yes for high end only	y	5	2	

Changes: *Leachlines under raised beds, a 20+ year old design, was moved from the roster of system options to the list of common errors (page 44) due to chronic clogging and distribution evenness problems. The "anti-septic tank" was deleted, the "multi-mode tank" added. "Septic tank and eco chambers" was replaced with "Septic tank and infiltrators."*

Comment	Greywater Sources: Laundry, Dishwasher	Tub, Shower, Bathroom Sink	Kitchen Sink	Toilet (blackwater) capable	Cost Range (*Not including collection plumbing. If needed, this will cost at least $50-$100 in parts and $100-$500 in labor.)	Requires Electricity?	Adapted for Freezing?	Suitable for Institutional Use?	% Irrigation Efficiency low/hi (Drip = 80%)	Degree of Filtration	Pages to read (b= Builder's GW Guide)
ɜood place to start	m	m	y		$0				30/80	None	12, 20
ɜood place to start		y			$0				10/50	None	12
ɜood for earthy life-style		y			$0-$1,000+		m		20/40[c]	None	12, b15-16
/ery simple, easy, reliable, cheap	y	y	y		$5-$10		m		10/40[c]	None	12, 26
imple, reliable: **most recommended system**[e]	y	y	y		$50-$1000*		m		30/60[c]	None	13, 26,b11-14
imple, efficient	y	y	y		$50-$100*				10/50	None	14, 26
imple, efficient, very popular for ιundry only	y	y			$20-$100				10/50	None to coarse	14, 27
mple way to water slightly uphill or on level	y	y			$20-$40				10/50	None	14, 27
ɔpular, but maintenance is unpleasant, ‹ely to be abandoned	y	y			$150-$350*	y			10/50	Coarse to medium	15, 16
ɔpular, maintenance is unpleasant, likely be abandoned, minimum legal system	y	y			$200-$1,300*	y		y	30/50[c]	Coarse to medium	16, 17
ɛs clever method of solving root encroachment	y	y	y		$500*	y	y	y	20/30[c]	Medium	18
quires batch dosing, can be gravity pumped	y	y	y		$100-$300*	m	y	y	10/30[c]	None to medium	19
›od for serious gardeners with energy for ɔving GW & strictly limited water supply	y	y	y		$50-$300*		m		10/80[d]	None	20
ssibility of destroying leachfield scary, but ne have worked flawlessly for decades	y	y	y	y	$0		y	y	10/20[a,c]	Fine (by settling)	21, 42
ry promising, unproven system	y	y	y	y	Septic tank +$200-$1,000		y	y	20/30[c]	Fine (by settling)	22
ven treatment technology. w to use for irrigation?	y	y	y	y	$5,000-$30,000	**Y**	y	y	10/50	Fine (by settling and sand)	21, 22
t system for cold climates. An asset to a l climate home in many ways	y	y	y		$100-$300* + greenhouse	m	**Y**	y	10/70[c]	None or fine	22, 31, 35
›t common in wet climates, familiar to ılators, expensive	y	y	y	y	$300-$15,000*			**Y**	10/50	Coarse to fine	23
›orate mechanics soothe health officials. .Y PROVEN SAFE WAY TO WATER TURF	y	y	y		$2,000-$6,000*	**Y**		**Y**	60/80	Very fine	24

Old name > New name

Drain out back > Drain to mulch basin

t drain or hard plumbing to m-l > Branched drain to mulch basins or leach chambers

Enhanced drain out back > Movable drain to mulch basins

Notes: (a) *water path unknown;* ***(b)*** *water path may be unknown;* ***(c)*** *water path cannot easily be changed;* ***(d)*** *depends on use mode;* ***(e)*** *see "Branched Drain Greywater Systems," inside back cover.*

System Examples

Unsatisfactory Systems

There is much entrenched greywater misinformation out there, and many common errors people reinvent independently. Publishing accurate, up-to-date information hasn't made much of a dent, so we've added a compendium of greywater misinformation and common errors which explains where the logic went wrong and suggests alternatives (see page 40—this section is highly recommended reading. There is also a continually updated version on our web site). Here's one common error, to whet your appetite:

Garden hose direct from the back of the washer

This method works until any of these problems occur: 1) the hose kinks and the washer pump burns out; 2) the pump, after months of working harder, burns out; 3) scalding hot water boils your prized plant; 4) the machine tries to refill itself and the hose (with its end lower than the washer) siphons fresh water out until someone shuts off the washer; 5) the pump doesn't get all of the water out so clothes stay soggy, or 6), you lift the hose to move it to a new mulch basin and weeks-old fetid greywater rushes backwards into the machine and onto your clothes. **Preferred practice:** The *drumless laundry system* (page 14) solves all of these problems except the hot water one. The *gravity drum*, (page 15) solves all these problems. **Exceptions:** As with many greywater errors, a certain percentage of "erroneous" installations are used for years without any of these problems manifesting. A significant percentage of people get away with this "error" because of a favorable confluence washing machine internal plumbing and site geometry, as the incidence of each individual error is fairly low. If you have an installation like this which has been working for years, why rock the boat? On the other hand, if you're installing a new system or replacing your old one, why not go straight for a design which is sure to work?

Systems That Work

A minimalist system (the first seven listed below) may be the best option. These systems are probably the most ecological, as they take little material to construct and no energy to operate. Due to their simplicity, they are reliable. The remaining systems are more complicated and expensive, but can offer more efficiency or convenience.

Dishpan dump

The most venerable of all greywater systems: when the dishpan water gets dirty, dump it in a flower bed. For those rare applications where water is truly precious, gardens need irrigation, and people have energy to haul buckets around daily, no system can equal the efficiency attainable by bucketing, even at a thousand times the cost.

Garden hose through the bathroom

In the bath or shower, block the drain with a flat rubber drain stopper. Use warm-u water to start a siphon, then run the water out of the bottom of the tub or shower stall into the garden after you bathe or as you shower.

Landscape direct

Consider—perhaps the mistake was to plumb the water into the house in the first place! Landscape direct greywatering is as simple as showering under a fruit tree with the garden hose or as beautiful as an elaborately landscaped bathing grotto in the midst of a food jungle—my specialty. It may slip through a legal loophole: because the water never enters a drain, it may not fit the definition of "wastewater." The most refined landscape direct systems use variations in topography and sometimes imported materia with special permeability characteristics (such as sand or clay) to direct runoff efficientl to carefully sited plants[14] (see photo at left, figure, page 1).

Greywater from a shower in Fiji waters bananas, cocos, taro, etc.

Drain to mulch basin

Caution: Applying greywater too near the foundation may cause problems in clay soils.

FIGURE 2: DRAIN TO MULCH BASIN

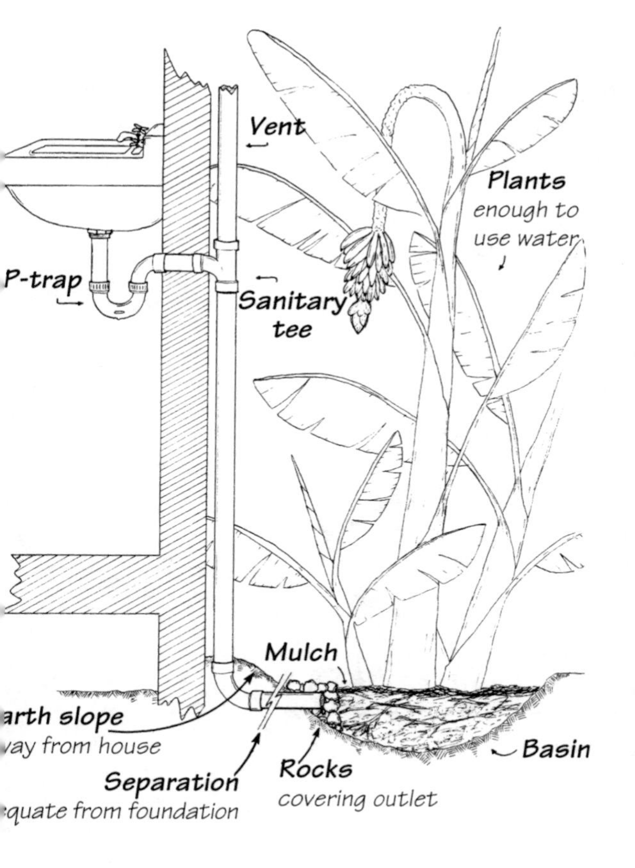

Probably 90% of the greywater systems in the world are just drains which point out the back. Some are gross and most don't reuse the water for irrigation. The simple refinement of adding a mulch-filled basin where the pipe dumps will eliminate virtually all grossness, and if there are plants there whose irrigation needs match the water source, it will efficiently reuse the water. Cover the greywater outlet with rocks and mulch, and install vent and p-trap unless you want the true back-woods feel, complete with flying insects and vermin entering the house via the drain pipe (an s-trap would be a compromise between a p-trap and no trap; see glossary). The lines can run any distance with *proper slope* (at least 1/4" per foot).

Branched drain to mulch basins or mini-leachfields

Caution: it is critical that hard-plumbed lines have proper slope. Double ells have worked extremely well in limited trials.

This is the system I recommend most frequently. An Art Ludwig original, it uses "double ells" for splitting the flow (see figure at lower left). For sites with continuous downhill slope between the greywater source and irrigated area the double ell design promises inexpensive, reliable, automated distribution with almost no maintenance. For plans to design and construct it in just about any context see our *Branched Drain Greywater Systems* manual (inside back cover).

It is possible to do four successive two-way splits. In theory, the water will split predictably so a single irrigation zone sensor would get a representative reading from any outlet. Another way to split the greywater flow and accomplish wider distribution is to not combine the flows in the first place: each fixture waters its own area. *Coordination with fresh water irrigation may be complicated by using this technique.*A friendly inpsector can easily approve a permit for the subsurface version of this system under the California or Uniform Plumbing Code (photo, page 25).

BRANCHED DRAIN TO MINI-LEACHFIELDS (PLAN VIEW)

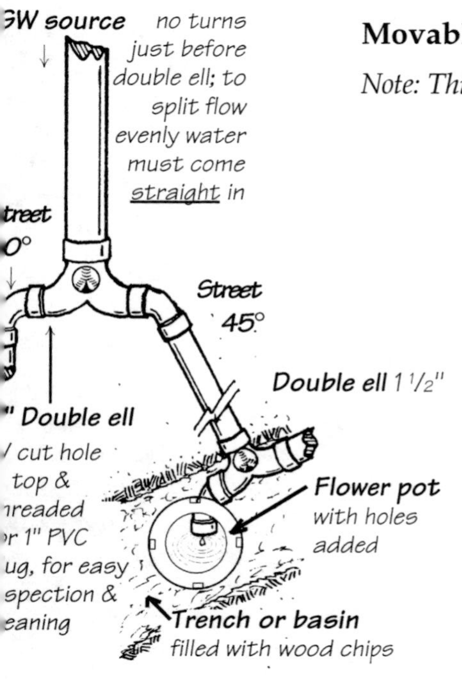

Movable drain to mulch basins

Note: This system has worked very well, but trials have not been extensive.

This is another Art Ludwig original. The design (see Figure 3, page 14) is appealing in its simplicity. Splice a diverter valve[s3] into the collection plumbing and route a standard ABS waste line at 1/4" per foot slope out the side of the house into the yard, to the edge of a mulch basin where water is needed. Water runs into this basin or is routed to another downhill basin through 1" flexible PVC (spa-flex).[s4]

Flexible PVC is inexpensive, makes nice sweeping curves and is impossible to kink. The dark brown version looks better snaking around the yard than the common brilliant white variety. Fifty-foot lengths are joined with press-fit PVC fittings or joined against leaks and tension with PVC field repair couplings. One inch is a large enough diameter for a tub to drain tolerably quickly, *eliminating the need for a surge tank.* The collection plumbing for this type of system is tedious and

Flexible PVC —a working tinkertoy set for moving water or wastewater without glue (or leaks) at pressures up to 20 psi.

expensive (as gravity collection plumbing always is), but the system is simplicity itself in operation. All of the crud that chokes filtered systems flows harmlessly ou into the landscape and becomes compost. There is a bit of a learning curve for layir spa-flex, the same as for the hose from a "gravity drum." Hose lengths should be no longer than needed, and the slope as constant as possible so air and water can drain freely. The main obstacle that stops flow is an "air lock," where air's buoyancy traps it an inverted U section and blocks the flow of water. Right-side-up U's appear to w fine, at least with low-solids, high-volume greywater.

FIGURE 3: MOVABLE DRAIN TO MULCH BASINS

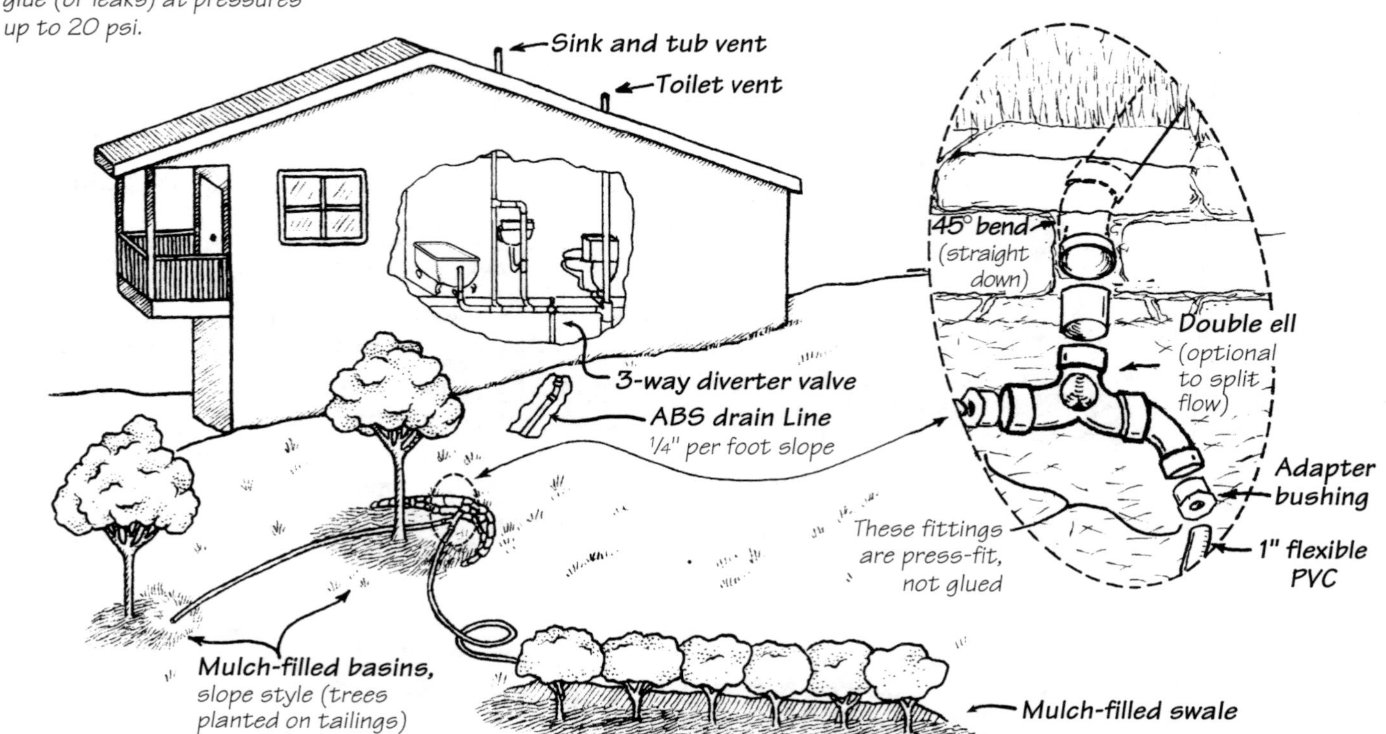

Gravity drum

With this system (see Figure 4, page 15; photo page 27) even distribution is a achieved by moving the hose from basin to basin. This deceptively simple approa elegantly solves a host of problems, in exchange for one ongoing task—someone l to move the hose every day or two to another mulch basin. If you're a person wh spends time in the garden and will move the hose, seek no further—this is the mos reliable, bombproof way of delivering laundry greywater to your plants and requir virtually no maintenance, decade after decade. The same distribution system coul be connected to collection plumbing from the shower, bath, etc.

Drumless laundry system

Note: This system has worked very well, but trials have not been extensive or long-term. Expect the washer pump life to be shortened proportionally to the extra load added to it.

The impossibility of kinking flexible PVC tubing enables a washer to be connect to it in direct drive without fear of it kinking and frying the washing machine pur This system (see Figure 5, page 16) saves space since it does not require a surge ta It is also uniquely able to use the washing machine's internal pump to pump wat

FIGURE 4: GRAVITY DRUM

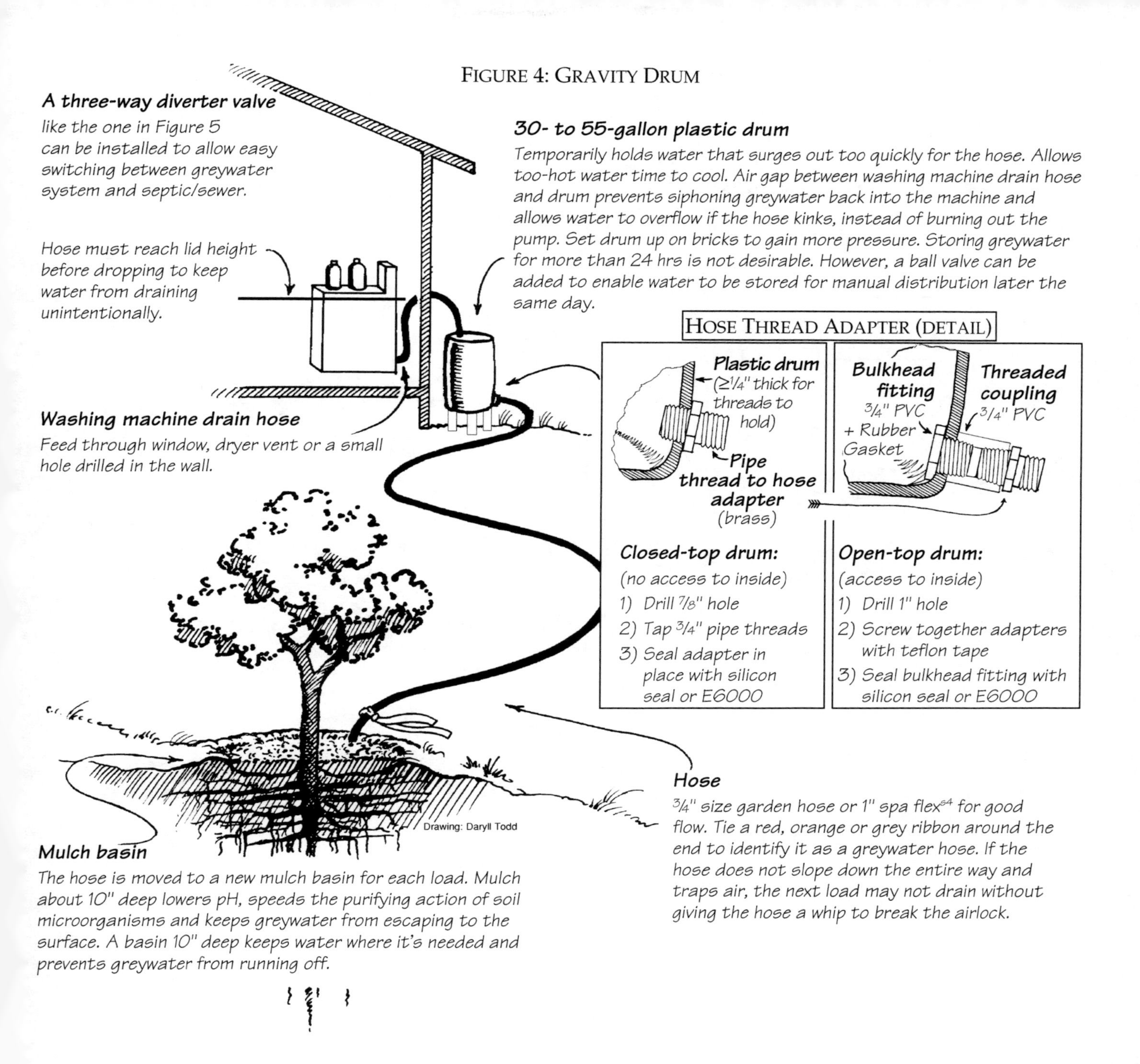

some distance away, to the height of the top of the washer, with barely more load than normal. It can go three to five feet higher if you don't mind risking damage to the pump (see also *Collection plumbing for pressurized greywater sources*, page 27).

A three-way diverter valve
like the one in Figure 5 can be installed to allow easy switching between greywater system and septic/sewer.
30- to 55-gallon plastic drum
Temporarily holds water that surges out too quickly for the hose. Allows too-hot water time to cool. Air gap between washing machine drain hose and drum prevents siphoning greywater back into the machine and allows water to overflow if the hose kinks, instead of burning out the pump. Set drum up on bricks to gain more pressure. Storing greywater for more than 24 hrs is not desirable. However, a ball valve can be added to enable water to be stored for manual distribution later the same day.
Hose must reach lid height before dropping to keep water from draining unintentionally.
HOSE THREAD ADAPTER (DETAIL)
Plastic drum
(≥1/4" thick for threads to hold)
Pipe thread to hose adapter
(brass)
Bulkhead fitting
3/4" PVC
+ Rubber Gasket
Threaded coupling
3/4" PVC
Closed-top drum:
(no access to inside)
1) Drill 7/8" hole
2) Tap 3/4" pipe threads
3) Seal adapter in place with silicon seal or E6000
Open-top drum:
(access to inside)
1) Drill 1" hole
2) Screw together adapters with teflon tape
3) Seal bulkhead fitting with silicon seal or E6000
Washing machine drain hose
Feed through window, dryer vent or a small hole drilled in the wall.
Hose
3/4" size garden hose or 1" spa flex[s4] for good flow. Tie a red, orange or grey ribbon around the end to identify it as a greywater hose. If the hose does not slope down the entire way and traps air, the next load may not drain without giving the hose a whip to break the airlock.
Drawing: Daryll Todd
Mulch basin
The hose is moved to a new mulch basin for each load. Mulch about 10" deep lowers pH, speeds the purifying action of soil microorganisms and keeps greywater from escaping to the surface. A basin 10" deep keeps water where it's needed and prevents greywater from running off.

Drum with pump, filter

Caution: The design details of this type of system greatly impact their reliability. Most have been abandoned due to maintenance hassles, even when constructed well.

If your garden is downhill from the drum, which may be up to five feet higher than the washing machine, a gravity drum that costs $20 to $100 is best. Otherwise, a sump pump capable of passing solids and a back flow prevention valve are needed, for another $150 to $200[s5] (see Figure 6, page 17; photo page 30). To prevent hair from wrapping around the pump rotor, pantyhose can be tied to the inlet as a filter. Many people discard the inexpensive pantyhose rather than clean them.

FIGURE 5: DRUMLESS LAUNDRY SYSTEM

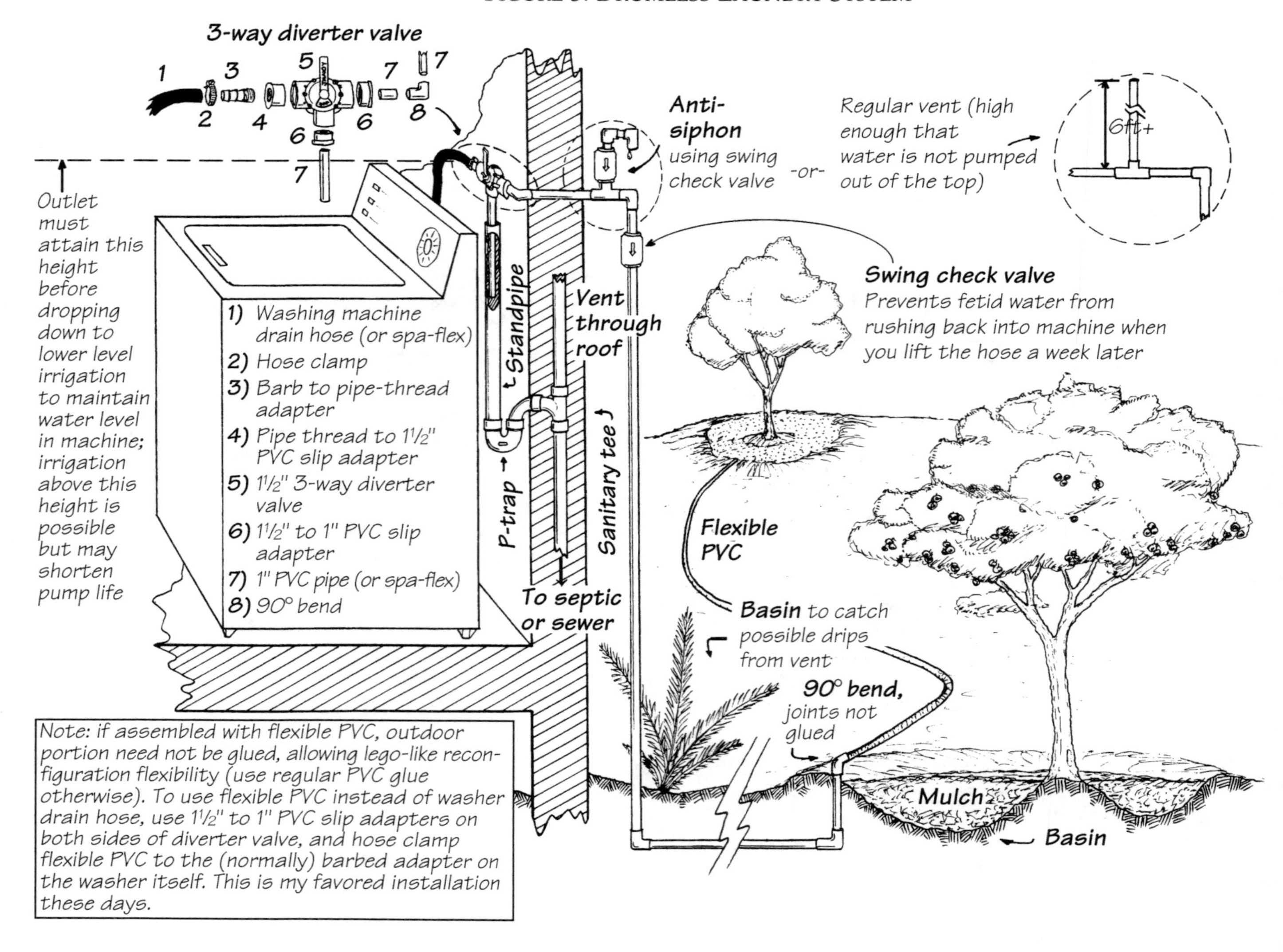

This degree of filtering allows reliable greywater distribution through inexpensive ½" drip tubing, using ½" plastic in-line drip ball valves to direct the flow to a number of watering fields. Each field can have two to six ½" openings with reasonably even flow, which lead to mulch basins or "mini-leachfields" (see Figure 7).

Mini-leachfields offer somewhat even subsurface irrigation at a reasonable price. The original version by Larry Farwell, the man largely responsible for the legalization of greywater in the state of California, uses a tee, a short length of ½" tubing that protrudes through the bottom of an inverted flower pot, and another tee on the end to keep it from pulling out of the pot. The mini-leachfields described in the California greywater law are completely buried, with gravel directly under the emitter. For those who, like myself, are concerned about checking for clogs and unenthusiastic about shoveling gravel into the garden, mini-leachfields could be filled to the top with wood chips in place of gravel, filter fabric, and soil.

If you have enough slope, mini-leachfields with ½" (minimum) orifices can be fed by gravity, with or without a filter, depending on whether you'd rather clean clogs or filters. For a gravity system, the number of ½" openings that can be supplied simultaneously drops from six to two, which also must be at equal elevation.

FIGURE 6. DRUM WITH PUMP, FILTER

Split from a 1" drumless laundry line to six 1/2" lines which feed separate mulch basins. In this nearly untested but promising design, pressure from the washer pump yields fairly even splitting, especially with the outlet heights and line lengths approximately equal.
With more lines some might clog with lint due lower pressure per line. Fewer lines might put too much load on the pump, especially if one or more kink—six 1/2" lines carry only slightly more water than one 1" line.
This should also work for a drum with pump & filter or a drum with solids-capable pump and no filter.

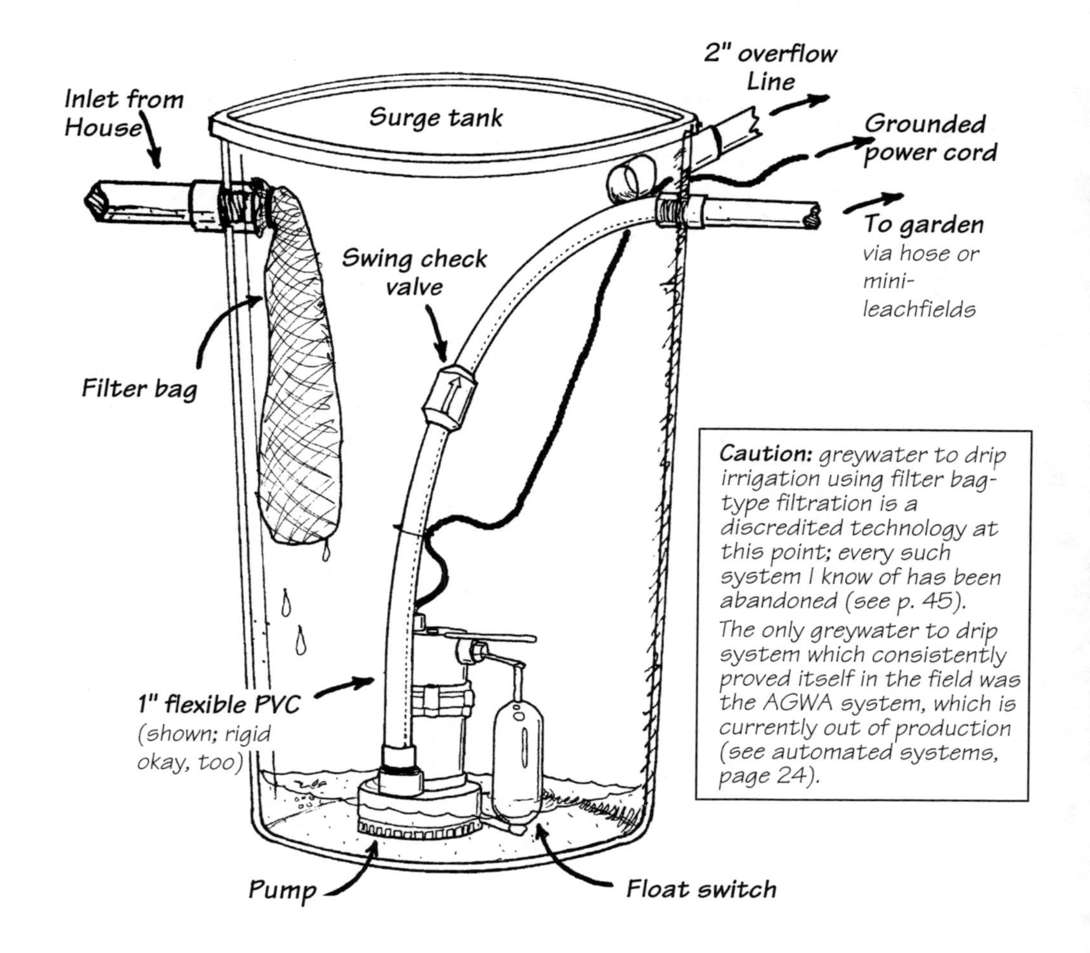

Caution: *greywater to drip irrigation using filter bag-type filtration is a discredited technology at this point; every such system I know of has been abandoned (see p. 45).*
The only greywater to drip system which consistently proved itself in the field was the AGWA system, which is currently out of production (see automated systems, page 24).

FIGURE 7: MINI-LEACHFIELD

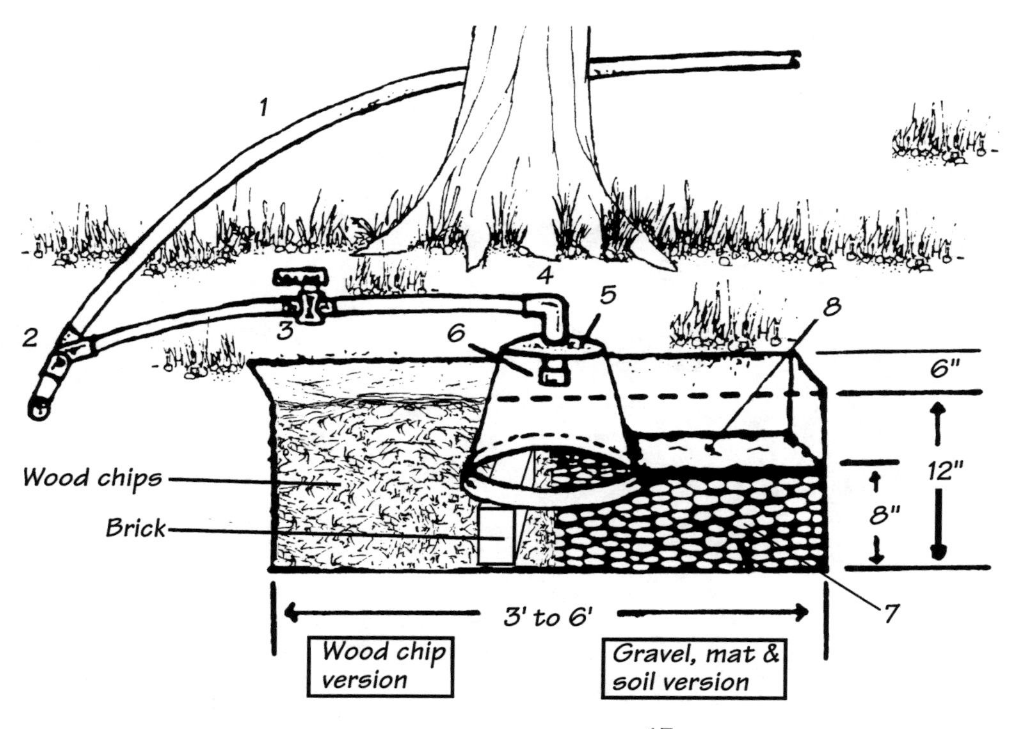

1) 1/2" Polyethylene Irrigation Hose
2) Tee Coupler
3) 1/2" Barbed Plastic Ball Valve
4) 90° Bend
5) Clay or Plastic Pot
6) Coupling (keeps line from pulling out of pot)
7) 1" Gravel
8) Weed-Stop Matting or Building Paper

FIGURE 8: DISTRIBUTION CONE

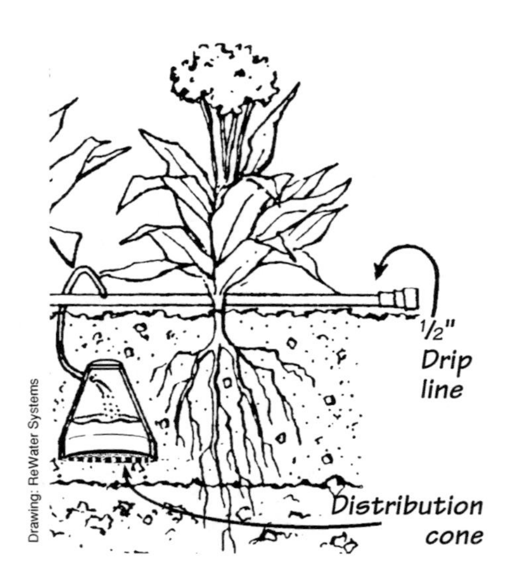

ReWater Systems[s6] has developed one-piece recycled plastic distribution cones (Figure 8) which are approved by the Center for Irrigation Technology, as required by the new California greywater law. It may turn out to be a cheaper and more convenient version of the mini-leachfield. The cones supposedly don't require gravel and can be supplied with 3/4", 1/2" or 1/4" drip tubing. The smaller aperture requires consistent filtration, but yields more even, extensive distribution.

Infiltration Beds

These plant beds filter & purify the water they don't transpire, much like a constructed wetland. Cleverly designed nested pipes by Clivus Ecological Resource Recovery[s7] (Figure 9) dribble water evenly along their lengths when pressurized to 5 to 10 psi (they won't work without a pump), then clamp shut to keep out roots when the pressure shuts off. Installing them on top of the soil (under mulch) helps to discourage roots, too. They require medium, pantyhose-type prefiltration. Discharge from soilbeds can be distributed subsurface without becoming septic or forming a clogging mat. Hundreds of these have been in use in New England since the 1970s.

FIGURE 9: INFILTRATION BED

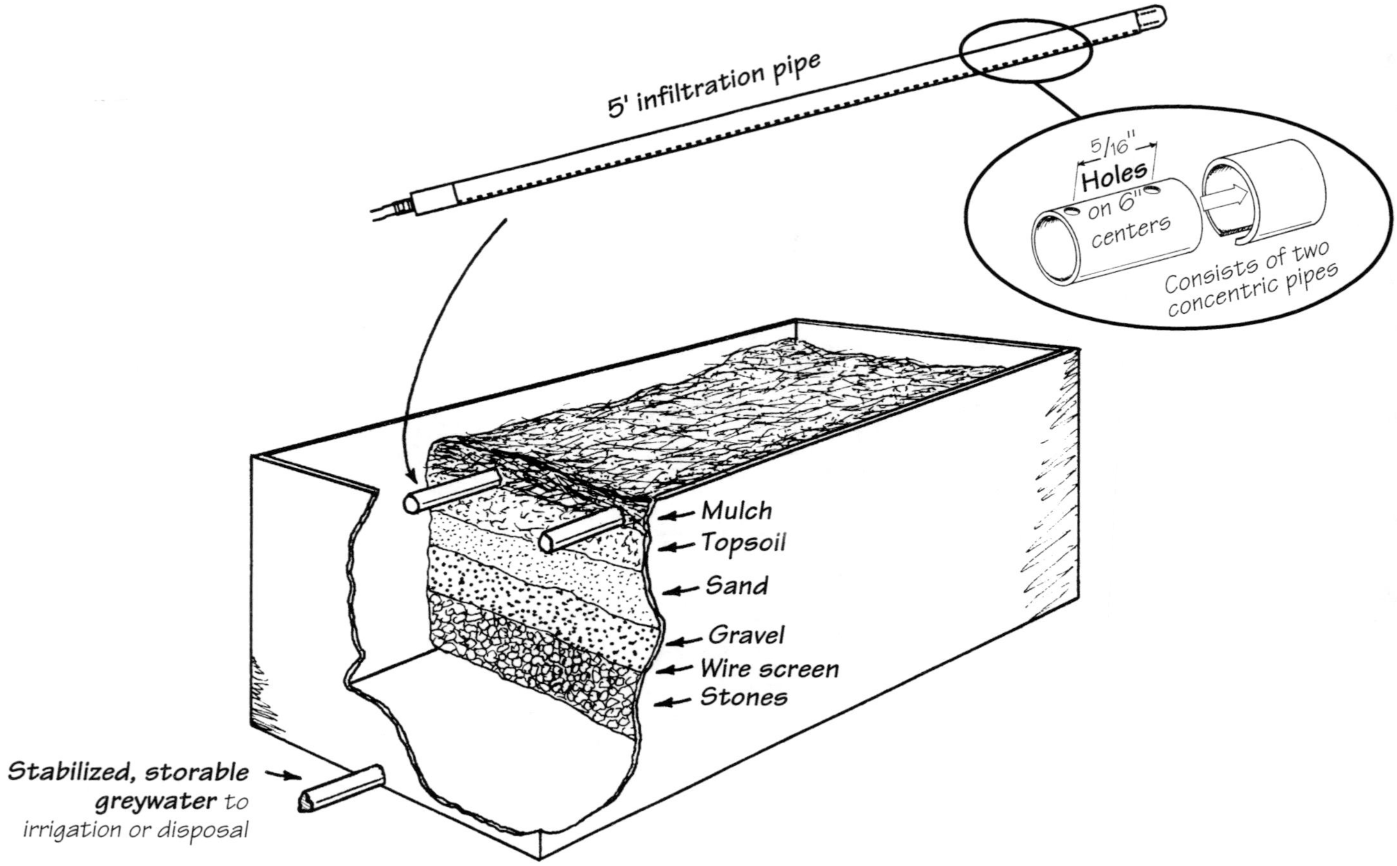

Leaching chambers, box trough

One simple way to distribute greywater subsurface is by sending it out under 6" to 8" pipes cut in half lengthwise (Figure 10). The half-pipes rest on 1" plastic mesh to keep them from sinking into the soil, and are covered with mulch. These do not require filtration, although an impermeable biomat may form without active earthworms. The pipe must be very carefully laid on a level surface and *dosed in large batches for even distribution* (see *Surge Capacity*, page 30). The optimal-sized surge would fill the entire trench 1½" deep. *Dosing will avoid an accumulation of solids right at the inlet, which can lead to progressive failure as successive small areas are overwhelmed with solids.*[s8]

FIGURE 10: LEACHING CHAMBER

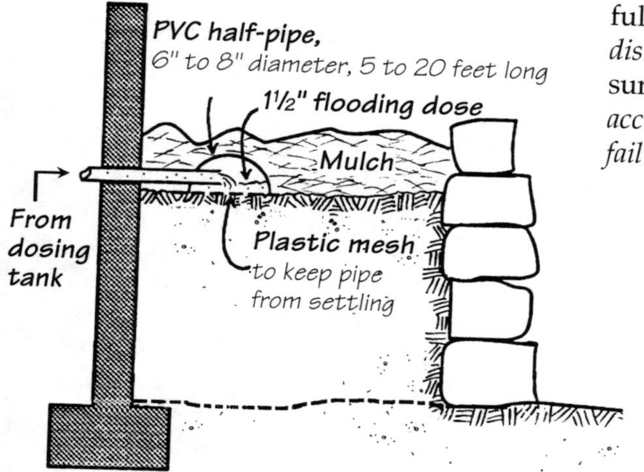

DESIGN LOADING RATES (CONSERVATIVE; CAN BE UP TO 3-5 GAL/DAY/FT²)

Soil infiltration rate, min/in	Loading rate gal/day/ft²	Area needed ft²/gal/day
0-30	2.5	0.4
40-45	1.5	0.7
45-60	1.0	1.0
60-120	0.5	2.0

Box troughs water a greywater greenhouse in Maryland.

A variation with easier maintenance access is a trough with a removable lid:

FIGURE 11: BOX TROUGH

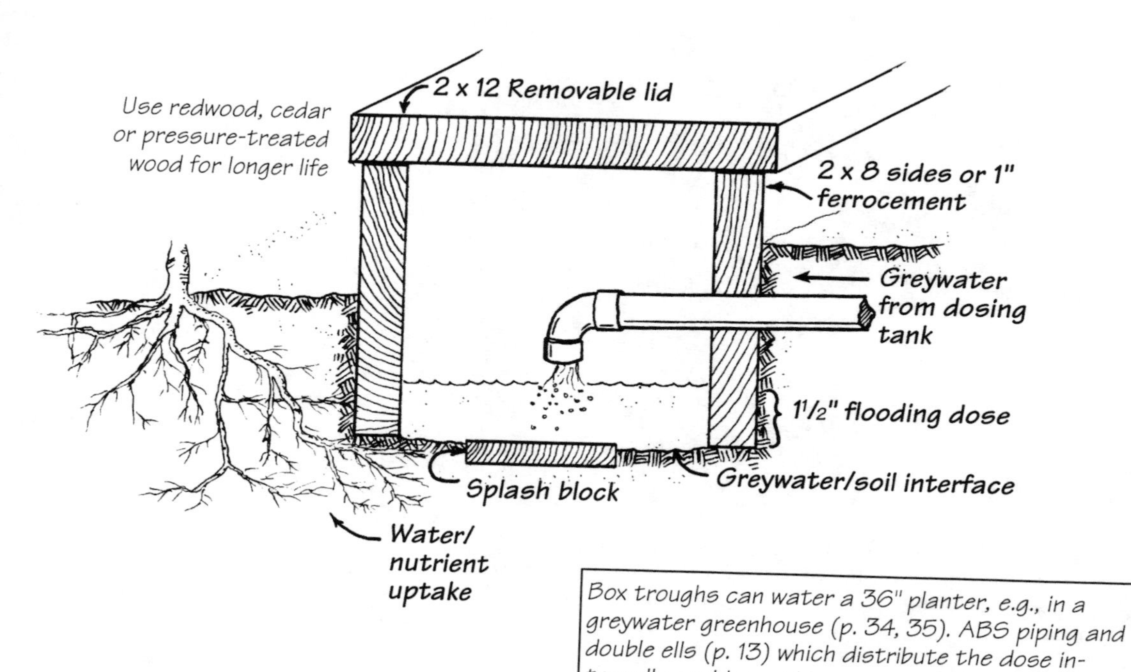

Box troughs can water a 36" planter, e.g., in a greywater greenhouse (p. 34, 35). ABS piping and double ells (p. 13) which distribute the dose internally could possibly be concealed inside the box.

Multi-mode greywater tank

Caution: This is a new design. It is working well but trials have been limited and short term. It doesn't even have a good name yet!

I developed this system for a site with an eight month, dust-dry season when the only water is from storage in cisterns, followed by four feet of rain in four months! The arrangement is a hybrid of proven designs. The application is anywhere water for gardens is precious, people are not prudish about hygiene, and have energy to bucket greywater. The system has four use modes, depending on the irrigation efficiency desired:

WARNING!
Unattended buckets with even a few inches of water are a drowning hazard for little kids.

- ❖ Bucketing—80% efficiency, considerable effort. Pairs of buckets are filled from the tank and manually doled out to plants (a five gallon bucket per square yard of irrigated area is about an inch of water; an inch per week is a typical irrigation level). An added benefit of bucketing mode is that whoever is emptying the tank(s) is acutely aware of how much water is being used indoors. This can improve indoor conservation. On average, people who carry water *to* their homes use 10% as much as people with piped water. Carrying water *out* of the home should have a similar effect, and the energy is more effectively applied as pipes can't distribute wastewater to plants nearly as well as they supply potable water.
- ❖ Manual hose—65% efficiency, medium effort. Water is released from the tank once a day through a large-diameter hose with a valve at the end, which is moved by hand and shut off between watering areas.
- ❖ Semi-automatic hose—50% or less efficiency, low effort. The drain of the tank is left open and water runs through immediately out the hose to whatever plant is at the end of the line. The line is moved periodically between plants.
- ❖ Automatic hose—Near 0% efficiency, no effort. For the wet season, the hose is routed to a mulch-filled infiltration basin and just left there.

FIGURE 12: FERROCEMENT BUCKET-SCOOP ("CANOE") TANK

Overflow
At highest point. Overflow joins drain or just dumps to a nearby fruit tree.

Shape and texture
This tank is ferrocement with a smooth finish. The entire tank slopes 1/4" per foot (min) to the drain. The bottom and end curves match the lower third of a 5 gallon bucket to within 1/16". This enables all the water and crud to be scooped out very quickly and efficiently. The lid opening should be 20" by 55", with round ends to accommodate a natural bucket scoop. The depth can be varied; 20" is a good figure. The usable volume of the tank shown is 30 gallons.

Metal lid

Inlet
As high as possible

Tank extension
To attain daily greywater volume, shape and location of extension is unimportant so long as it drains to the low point.

Drain
At lowest point, in middle of bucket scoop. Plugged with recessed rubber stopper in bathtub drain with metal cross removed.

All the house's water could go to one tank, but if there are many greywater sources and an extensive irrigated area it is better to place multiple tanks around the garden in convenient locations. The tanks are sized to accommodate one day's high average greywater flow. There are two options for the shape, depending on the amount of fall available. If there is enough fall, the tank can be any shape (a plastic drum works) and buckets are filled by placing them under the drain line. If this extra two feet plus of fall is not available, it can be built with a special "canoe" shape I developed which enables the tank to be scooped empty quickly and completely by bucket (see photo at left). Topography permitting, it makes for less stooped-over bucketing if there is an area to stand several inches below the bottom of the tank.

Multi-mode greywater tank with enough fall to fill a bucket from a valve at the bottom. A quarter-cylinder shape, this tank fits nicely in an inside corner of a house in Mexico. It holds 50 gallons and is made out of ferro-cement faced with stone. The floor slopes strongly towards the outlet, so it drains completely of water and is self-cleaning of solids.

Plants over the septic tank leachfield

Caution: Taking advantage of the "grass is always greener over the septic system" phenomenon seems natural. However, mixed results have been obtained so far, especially using perforated pipe. It takes decades for this type of system to prove its reliability. The stakes of experimentation are high, as replacing a leachfield costs a bundle. Without a distribution box or flow splitters to split the flow, irrigation would be extremely uneven and untraceable. For a surer bet, try Septic tank and infiltrators, below.

If you already have a septic system and know where the leachfields are, you could plant there to take advantage of the water and nutrients. Be prepared to deal with de-rooting or abandoning the leachfield some day.

Septic tank, flow splitters and infiltrators

Caution: Infiltrators are proven for disposal. Configuring a system for even distribution and irrigation reuse is a very promising but unproven variation.

A septic tank finely filters wastewater without a mesh that can clog. It does this by settling. Stuff that is lighter than water floats to join the scum mat at the top, and heavier materials sink into the sludge at the bottom. Effluent from the middle stinks but is clear. To settle effectively, two or more days retention time is required. To avoid clogging the leachfield, size the tank generously for the flow (2-30 days retention) and pump solids out of the tank proactively, not after the system stops working.

If you must extend or replace your septic tank leachfield, or are building a new one, consider designing and building it especially to facilitate reuse, inspection and de-rooting.[16] Achieving even distribution of water is impossible with a gravity powered perforated pipe system. Instead, direct water through solid lines (no root infiltration) to a distribution box, then through solid lines and/or flow splitters to "infiltrators"[s10] in the vicinity of trees. (Figures 13, 14). The key is to evenly, predictably split the flow, and to bury the infiltrators as shallow as possible so roots can get at the water.

FIGURE 13: SEPTIC TANK, FLOW SPLITTERS AND INFILTRATORS
(NUTRIENT AND WATER REUSE FROM A NEARLY CONVENTIONAL SYSTEM)

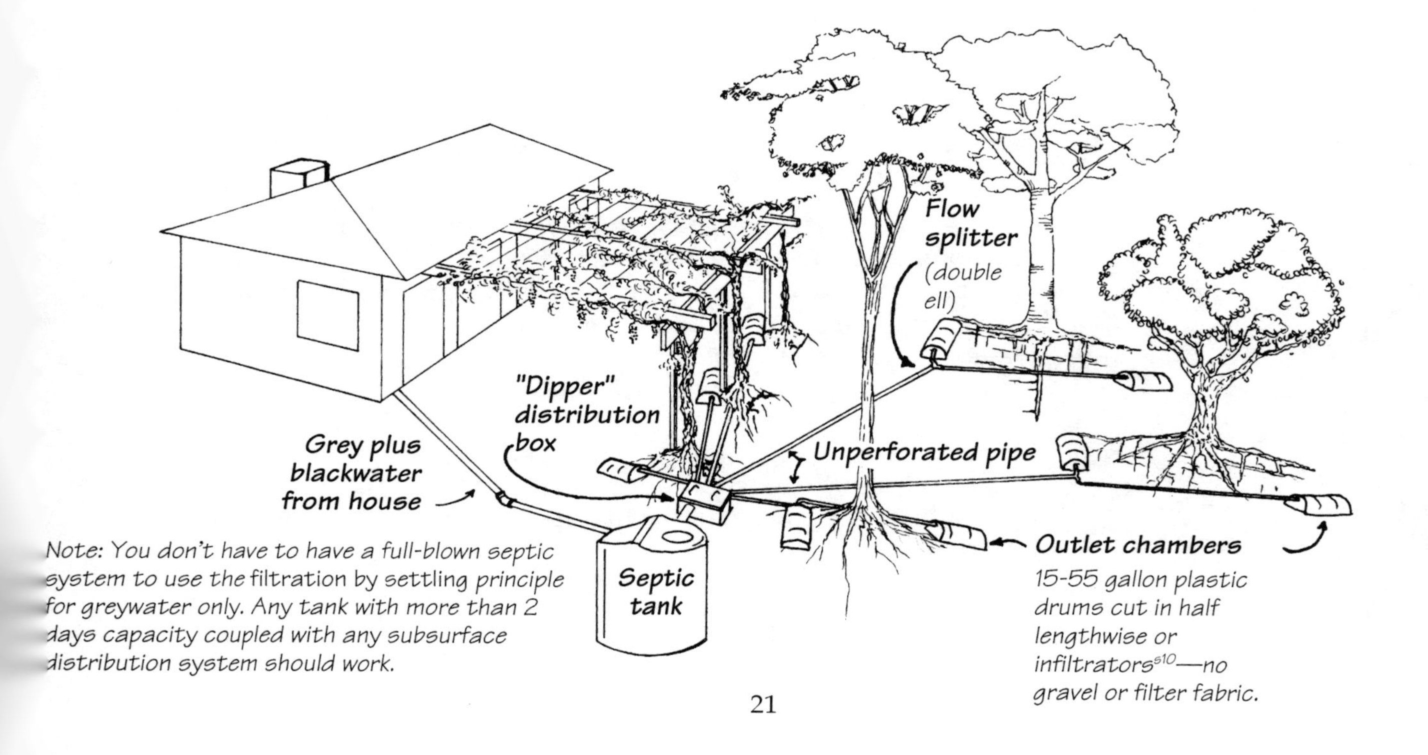
Flow splitter
(double ell)
"Dipper" distribution box
Grey plus blackwater from house
Unperforated pipe
Outlet chambers
15-55 gallon plastic drums cut in half lengthwise or infiltrators[s10]—no gravel or filter fabric.
Septic tank
Note: You don't have to have a full-blown septic system to use the filtration by settling principle for greywater only. Any tank with more than 2 days capacity coupled with any subsurface distribution system should work.

FIGURE 14: INFILTRATOR

Standard sidewinder infiltrator 17ft2, 76 gal

Infiltrators can be serviced or relocated much easier than gravel and filter fabric. To facilitate inspection and de-rooting, cut covered inspection/service ports in the chambers just above the outlet and periscope cleanouts at key points to the surface.

This type of system is not limited to greywater. It can recycle blackwater as well. Septic systems go for long periods without needing maintenance, and are *legal everywhere under existing building codes.* If you decide to reuse your greywater this way, I strongly suggest you never mention the word "greywater" to the inspector.

Septic tank and sand filtration

Caution: Well-proven as a treatment technology, but less common for reuse. This technology uses a lot of electricity.

Sand filtered effluent distributed through 1/2" PVC lines with 1/16" holes and emitter shields.

Filter septic tank effluent through sand, and trillions of bacteria growing aerobically on sand surfaces gobble the dissolved nutrients and anaerobic bacteria, yielding a sweet smelling, highly polished effluent. The water is still an infection hazard, but it will not clog drip irrigation hardware. Thus, the dream of nearly zero maintenance greywater-to-drip irrigation system can be achieved. It will cost several thousand dollars, but the majority would be spent on a septic tank and conventional drip irrigation system that you'd need otherwise. According to purveyors of sand filtration systems, the treatment level is such that toilet water doesn't have to be excluded. People also are experimenting with ozone disinfection, which one day may permit this water to be used for sprinklers or garden ponds.

As much as I dislike pumps, a pressure-dosing system with small diameter pipe or subsurface drip irrigation will distribute water far wider and more evenly than a gravity system. Orenco Systems[s9] suggests using a sewage ejector pump for leachline laterals up to 100 feet long, constructed of 1/2" PVC with 1/16" holes on 1 foot centers and a 1" PVC pipe with 1/8" holes on 1 foot centers slipped over it. Roots supposedly air prune in the space between the concentric pipes.

Greywater Greenhouse

Note: Successful in limited trials with infiltration beds supplied by drum with pump; box troughs supplied by gravity through double ells is a promising but untried variation.

No finer synergy can be obtained between the different systems of a home than in a solar greywater greenhouse (page 35). Compared to irrigation need outdoors, irrigation need in a greenhouse is relatively constant throughout the year, as is greywater supply. Greywater treatment may be feasible in a greenhouse when it wasn't outdoors. A solar greenhouse can dramatically reduce space heating requirements.

Greywater can be supplied to three-foot-wide raised infiltration beds (page 18) via drum with pump and filter (page 17), or box troughs (page 19), possibly supplied by ABS piping with the flow split in double ells[14] (contact us for the latest on this last design, which is untried as yet).

Greenhouse with Clivus infiltration beds in Massachusetts.

Constructed wetlands

Note: Proven for cleaning up large flows of partially treated municipal wastewater and residential septic tank effluent. Less common but successful for raw household greywater by itself; there are questions about clogging, high oxygen demand and nutrient balance. Systems are reported to work with panty hose pre-filtration or a large area infiltrator at the inlet (see below), but a septic tank is better proven. Design guidance from an engineer with constructed wetland experience is highly recommended.[s14, 19]

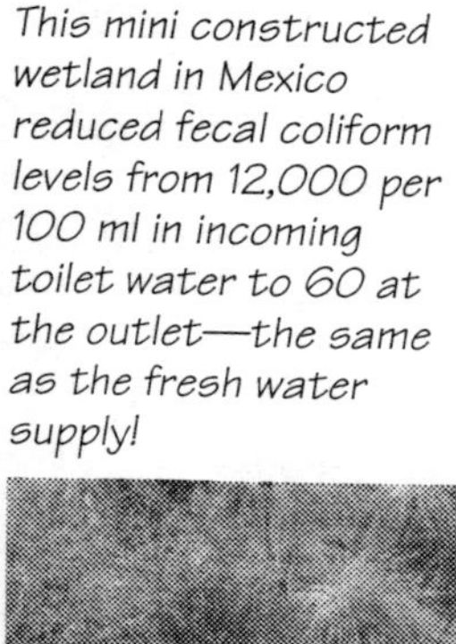

This mini constructed wetland in Mexico reduced fecal coliform levels from 12,000 per 100 ml in incoming toilet water to 60 at the outlet—the same as the fresh water supply!

There are two families of constructed wetland; one with open water and one with the water surface hidden under gravel, with plants coming up out of it (Figure 15).[6] Common sense would dictate that the hidden surface-type of system be used for greywater, at least for the first stage of treatment.

Constructed wetlands make sense for responsible disposal of greywater in wet climates and where perk is low, and for treatment of larger flows prior to reuse. Reuse efficiency is lowered considerably by water lost through wetland plants, especially when evapotranspiration is high and irrigation is needed most.

Wetland area is a complicated function of temperature, evapotranspiration, rainfall, influent volume and BOD (Biological Oxygen Demand; a measure of how much compost is in the water), and effluent requirements. One half to one square foot per gallon per day is typical. The plants function as solar-powered pumps which push oxygen out through the roots, and pull nutrients in. Their root hairs also provide the growth medium for beneficial microorganisms. Treatment is effective; however, disinfection may be required depending on what you do with the effluent.

Thanks to Southwest Wetlands and Tad Montgomery for help with the wetland section.

FIGURE 15: CONSTRUCTED WETLAND

Waterproof membrane
protected from sun (or construct wetland from cement). Unlined wetlands are an option in appropriate soil (low perk) and groundwater conditions (adequate separation).

Aquatic Plants
locally appropriate species

Water level
2" below surface of gravel, 12-30" deep depending on plant root depth; 12" for cattails, 24" for reeds, 30" for bulrushes

Drawing based on US EPA wetland manual

Rhizome network

Outlet manifold
covered with 1" rock

Treated water out

Infiltrator
2-3' wide half pipe or half drums covered with 1 1/2-3" rock, across width of wetland. Total wetland width should be about half of length

1/2-1" gravel
Uniform sized, double washed

Thermal baffles
Prevent short circuiting of effluent

Level control box
Pulling plug once a month lowers the water level, aerates and establishes roots in the lower part of system

Automated systems/ Sand filtration to subsurface drip irrigation

Caution: A halfhearted attempt at an automated system is doomed. Components that work reliably with wastewater are shockingly expensive, but anything less will fail.

Full automation is surprisingly complex. Unless you enjoy destroying expensive equipment as a hobby, breathe deeply and buy a system from an outfit that knows what they're doing, if you can find one.[s6, s9, s18] The only company I know that clearly fit this description was AGWA Systems, which made an excellent computer-controlled, automatic backwashing sand filter system (Figure 16). Unfortunately, the people at AGWA had to shift their energy to another business, and their system is out of production. Hopefully by the time you read this someone else will have picked up where they left off. Jade Mountain[s11] sells a copy which may be accurate. ReWater Systems[s6] and Orenco[s9] make possible substitutes. The AGWA system handled every conceivable aspect of greywater irrigation automatically—even coordinated it with freshwater irrigation! They have a good service record and their system was by far the best achievement in the high-tech genre. It cost between $1,100 and $8,000. The system worked reliably with drip irrigation, including underground drip, which is the only acceptable way to irrigate turf with greywater. For this system, the more greywater and irrigation needed, the better, in contrast to many others that can't really deal with volume. It starts to make sense with 200 gallons a day, but is really in its element with, say, an institution with laundry and shower facilities, and acres of irrigated area.

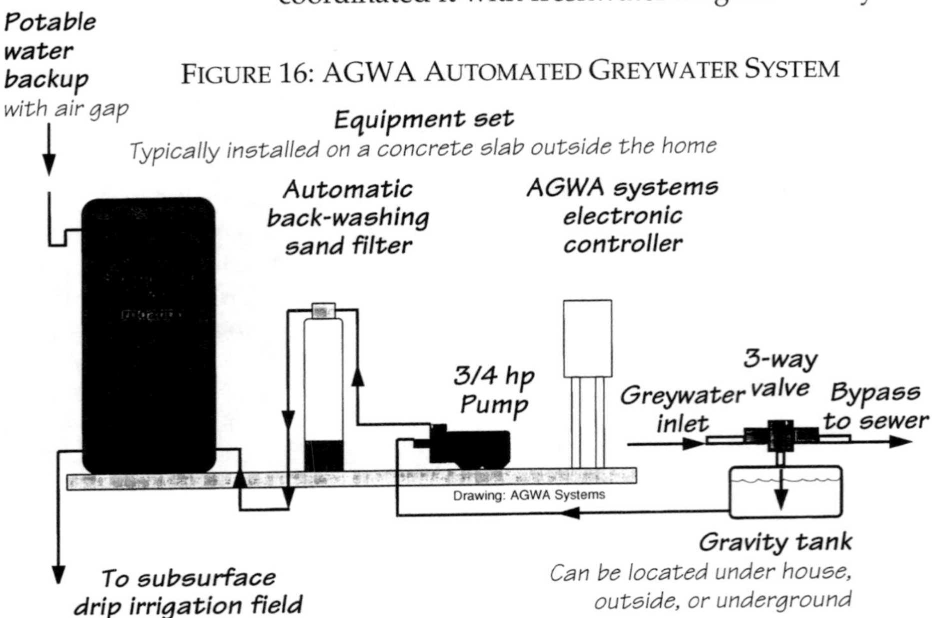

FIGURE 16: AGWA AUTOMATED GREYWATER SYSTEM

Plant and Soil Bio-compatible Cleaners

When you use greywater for irrigation, you have to think more about what you put down the drain. "Biodegradable" means that something breaks down, while "biocompatible" means these breakdown products are good for, or at least not harmful to, the environment in which they are disposed (see also *Biocompatibility Chart*, page 38).

Most of the substances which are necessarily part of household greywater biodegrade into plant nutrients. They include lint from natural fabrics, dead skin, sweat, hair, food particles, dirt, grime, etc. Household cleaners are the main exception. They vary in their toxicity to plants and soil, and different soil types and plants vary in their susceptibility. Few cleaners are so bad that they will immediately kill plants. Water is a big plus for thirsty plants, toxins from ordinary biodegradable cleaners are a small (but cumulative) minus, while nutrients from biocompatible cleaners[s15] are a small plus.

The requirements for biocompatibility depend on the environment to which the water is added. Salt doesn't hurt the ocean, but is toxic to plants and soil. Phosphorous is good for plants on land, but causes harmful algae blooms in the ocean. No-phosphate biodegradable detergents are designed not to hurt aquatic ecosystems but contain salt that will hurt the land.

Many people have experienced that insensitive plants may be watered for years with greywater containing non-biocompatible cleaning products. However, once damage is finally evident, it can be a really big job to repair the soil (see *Preserving Soil Quality*, page 37). Remembering that an ounce of prevention is worth a pound of cure:

- Avoid washing more often or using more cleaner than needed.
- Avoid cleaners that contain boron (borax), a potent plant toxin.
- Avoid using chlorine bleach or non-chlorine bleach containing sodium perborate. Liquid hydrogen peroxide is a less powerful, more expensive, but nontoxic alternative bleach.
- Use cleaners that contain little or no sodium. Liquid cleaners and laundry detergents contain less sodium than powders. A buildup of sodium is toxic to plants and destroys the structure of clay soils.
- Use plant and soil biocompatible cleaners, which contain no sodium, chlorine, or boron and do not adversely affect soil pH or structure.[s15]

Conclusion

The Future of Greywater Use

In the future, expect greatly expanded water recycling and options for legal greywater use, as underlying necessity erodes away attitudes and regulations which currently stifle advances in design and adoption for little reason.[2]

Commercial car washes and many industrial processes already purify their wastewater and reuse it. Reclaiming treated sewage for irrigation is exploding in popularity in the U.S. In Europe, highly treated sewage is pumped back into the potable water system. These systems take considerably more energy, chemicals and infrastructure than on-site reuse of untreated or partially treated greywater. As resource constraints tighten, home greywater systems will improve in efficiency, ease of maintenance and popularity. I predict that soon such systems, widely illegal only several years ago, will be mandated for new construction in some areas.

Taking full responsibility for the small part of the global water cycle which flows through the home is a good feeling. I hope the information in this book enables you to benefit more fully from the experiences others have had with greywater use, either to implement a proven design, or to pick up experimentation where others left off. If you experience notable success or failure with something you think should be in the next edition of this book, please drop me a line.

Permitted "branched drain to mulch basins" I installed in Santa Barbara as part of a State of California study.[15] The study showed that greywater systems saved water and did not have an adverse affect on soil quality. This system has been receiving only occasional inspection since its installation, and reliably distributes greywater to about two dozen fruit trees.

Pipes open inside inverted 5 gallon flower pots in large, deep basins, which are then backfilled completely with woodchips. The system is completely invisible in the landscape, yet easily serviced by pulling mulch back.

Appendix A

Greywater System Elements and Design Considerations In Detail

In this section, we delve into the details of elements that are common to many types of greywater systems. Be sure to note any mention in this chapter of special circumstances which pertain to your site.

Plumbing Principles

It is said that "plumbers safeguard the health of the nation." This is not an exaggeration. Don't let the prudish stance of the laws with respect to greywater delude you into thinking that *all* plumbing codes are for weenies. The place where plumbing codes lose credibility is in the garden, where greywater can be treated better and more ecologically than anywhere else. In the house, and on the way to the garden, deviate from code principles only when you know what you're doing, or you may be sorry. Since there isn't a well developed code for some of the strange things greywater users have to do, principles are explained below to help navigate your way through this *terra incognita.*

FIGURE 17: P-TRAP AND CRITICAL DISTANCE

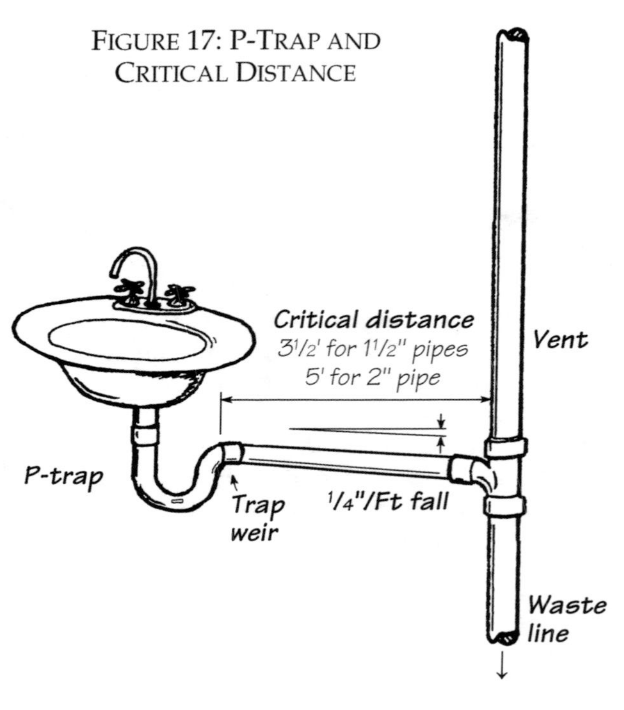

Traps and venting

The feature that most distinguishes modern plumbing from earlier, cholera epidemic era efforts is the vented p-trap, so named because it looks like a "P" on its side. The p-trap, by virtue of the small pocket of water it always holds, blocks all of the noxious gases and pernicious filth downstream from escaping back through the pipe into the house (Figure 17).

As is often the case with plumbing, careful distance, elevation and size relationships must be maintained to keep the p-trap from failing in an unforeseen mode. For instance, the p-trap must be vented just downstream, to break the vacuum created behind a flow of water that would otherwise siphon the little pocket of water right out of it. The vent must be within the "critical distance," so water filling the drainpipe won't block the path for air to get to the vent and create a mini-siphon just long enough to empty the p-trap.

The ideal venting for greywater collection is totally separate from the toilet vent. This eliminates the possibility for blackwater to back up through the common vent and into the greywater system. If this is impossible, tie into the toilet vent 12" above the spill point of the highest fixture served by the vent (see Figure 19, page 28).

FIGURE 18: SANITARY FITTINGS COMPARED TO SUPPLY FITTINGS

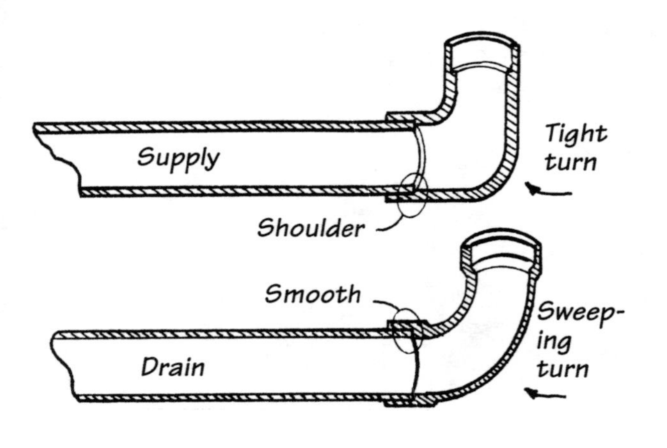

Fall and fittings

Tests with clear pipe have shown that unpressurized, crud-laden water flows best in pipes that are either *vertical* or *fall* $^{1}/_{4}$*" per foot* (2% slope). With shallower slope, water won't flow adequately, with steeper slope the water runs off quickly, leaving the crud behind. In practice, more fall seems to work OK for greywater. Less fall is bad. I often chip through concrete, replumb far upstream or whatever is necessary to get the right slope. Going uphill is out of the question, even for short distance. Avoid any U-shaped sections, as crud will surely settle in the U and block the pipe. Also, use smooth ABS drainpipe and fittings (Figure 18), which have no shoulder on the joints, and nice sweeping curves (exceptions: pressurized and/or filtered greywater, and greywater in flexible hoses which are moved periodically).

Collection plumbing for pressurized greywater sources

For pressurized greywater sources (washing machines, automatic dishwashers) collection plumbing can be as simple as shoving the outlet hose through a window or hole drilled in the wall to a surge tank or open discharge outside (see Figure 4, page 15; photo at left).

A "gravity drum" supplied by washer drain hose run through a 1" hole in the wall. Note this drum also catches rain water, which runs through a screen mesh and out through the same hose to flush salts from the mulch basins.

The outlet hose can be connected to 1" PVC pipe to make long pressurized runs. Each fifty feet adds about as much resistance as ten vertical inches. The resistance the pump has to overcome should ideally be about the same as in a standard installation, where the hose discharges at the height of the top of the machine. For example, if a washing machine empties through 100 feet of 1" pipe which ends 18" lower than its lid, the effective resistance is the same as if it discharged 2" above its lid, which is acceptable.

If the drainpipe opening is lower than the level of water in the washer, a *vacuum break* is required at the highest point to admit air and keep the drain line from continuously siphoning water out of the machine as it tries to refill itself. This is one reason the washing machine drain hose fits loosely into the standpipe in conventional plumbing. The line at the point of the vacuum break should be at the height of the washer lid; this prevents the water from draining by gravity. It is best to have the vacuum break opening into the old standpipe or outside; if the filter or distribution line clogs, the water will not gush through it onto the floor. Pumps in washing machines or dishwashers move a lot of water very fast, but not against much back pressure. Requiring such a pump to force water more than a few vertical feet invites premature pump failure.

If the drain line runs or can be lifted above the level of the top of the washer, a swing check valve should be included as close as possible to the washer to keep water in the line from rushing back into the machine when it shuts off.

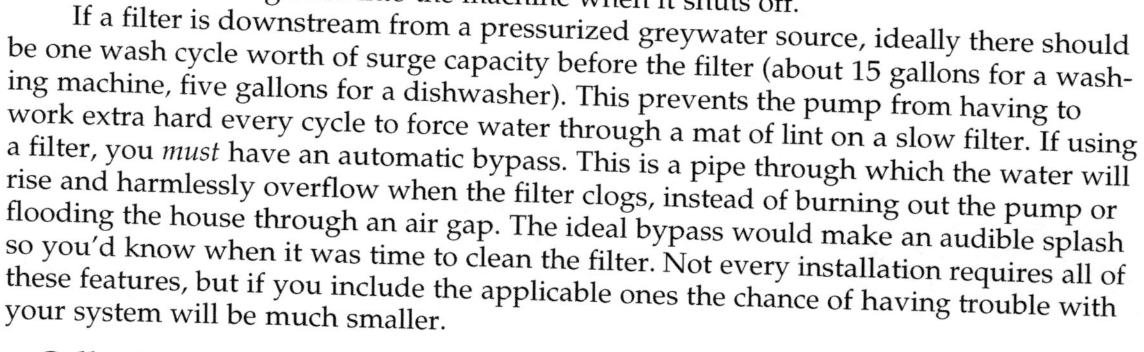

If a filter is downstream from a pressurized greywater source, ideally there should be one wash cycle worth of surge capacity before the filter (about 15 gallons for a washing machine, five gallons for a dishwasher). This prevents the pump from having to work extra hard every cycle to force water through a mat of lint on a slow filter. If using a filter, you *must* have an automatic bypass. This is a pipe through which the water will rise and harmlessly overflow when the filter clogs, instead of burning out the pump or flooding the house through an air gap. The ideal bypass would make an audible splash so you'd know when it was time to clean the filter. Not every installation requires all of these features, but if you include the applicable ones the chance of having trouble with your system will be much smaller.

Collection plumbing for gravity sources

Gravity collection plumbing (see Figure 19, page 28) transports greywater from the generation point to a common point. It is similar for most system types. To collect water from sinks, tub and shower, major replumbing is necessary. This may be fairly straightforward if drainpipes are easily accessed, or impossible if they are entombed under a concrete slab foundation. Often the amount of fall is insufficient to get greywater from existing drains to a surge tank by gravity. Even more likely is insufficient fall to get it from a surge tank overflow back to the septic tank or sewer line. In any case, using a **professional plumber to plan and execute collection plumbing is highly recommended.** Without the correct fall, venting and traps, the system may not drain satisfactorily or even be safe. It is surprisingly easy to build in cross connections—ways for greywater, blackwater and/or freshwater to mix when the system works in an unforeseen mode. In many areas, it is illegal to modify your own plumbing for these reasons. Collection plumbing is a good place to stick to code. An intelligent plumber unfamiliar with greywater can successfully do greywater collection plumbing. If you do want to tackle this yourself, refer to a plumbing book or have a plumber check your work.

For gravity sources, the plumbing that routes water from the fixtures to the outside will be conventional except in a few respects. First, in most installations, fall must be rigorously conserved. This impacts the design of every joint and pipe run, often making

FIGURE 19: HOW TO TIE IN COLLECTION PLUMBING

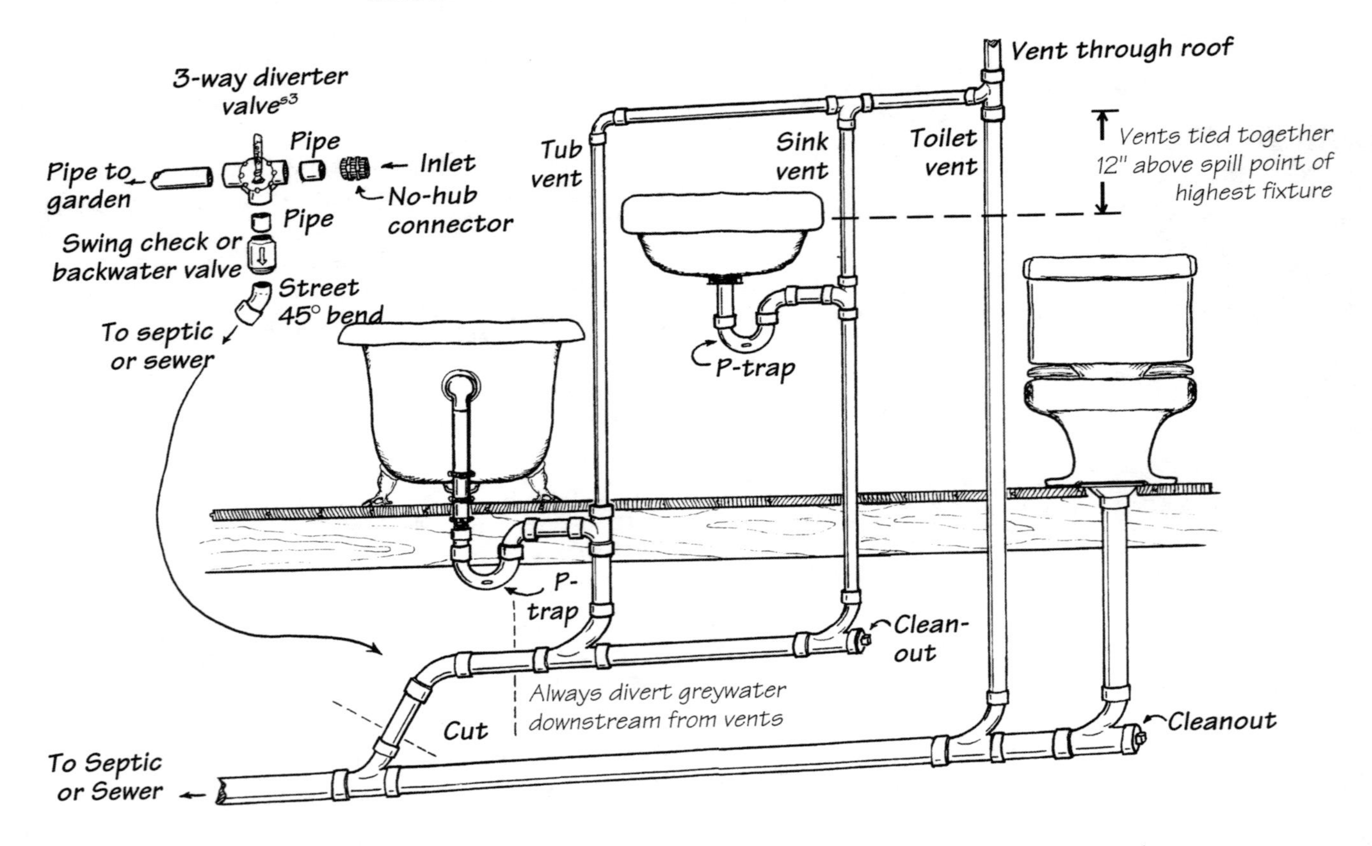

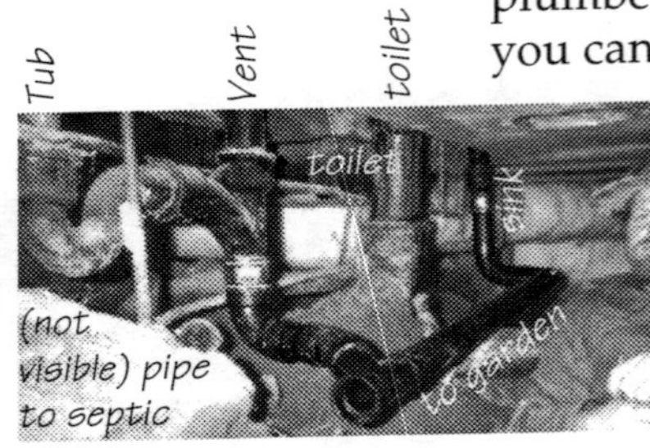

Sawing through cast iron drain lines and sending the greywater at greatest height possible in the opposite direction. The next fitting will be the three-way diverter valve, which then connects back to the septic tank, downstream of vents and traps.

them much more difficult and time-consuming. It is often necessary to hover over your plumber to insure that you end up with enough height when pipes exit the house. Then you can irrigate intensive plantings right around the house, where irrigation need is typically greatest, and not 100 feet away where the ground surface is finally low enough. Second, toilet water will be separate. If you are replumbing, I recommend *running greywater in separate pipes to the outside* even if you will join them there. This will give you flexibility to add a greywater system in the future. Diverter valves should be installed to enable greywater to be diverted to septic or sewer, in case the soil is waterlogged, the system is down, or you want to use some nasty cleaners which you don't want on your plants.

The diverter valve is always spliced in downstream from the fixture traps and vents, so they work both in greywater and septic tank/sewer modes. A backwater valve should be placed after the diverter valve on the line that connects to the septic or sewer to prevent the toilet from backing up into the greywater system.

Tools for Greywater Work

Tape measure
Levels (for gauging correct fall)
Hacksaw
ABS glue
Universal glue (ABS to PVC)
PVC cement
Drill and large bit or hole saw (to make holes for pipe to go through)
1/4" nutdriver or wrench (for tightening no-hub connectors)
Adjustable wrench

Optional tools

Transit or water level (for leveling across long distances)
Sawsall with metal cutting blade (to cut cast iron drain lines used in most pre-1970 homes)
Cordless drill (for pipe hangers)
Knife (to deburr pipe ends)
Narrow trench shovel (for running pipes underground to yard)
Pipe wrenches

Parts for Greywater Work

TABLE 3: GREYWATER PLUMBING PARTS

	Greywater Plumbing Application							Surge Capacity
	Gravity Collection	Pressure Collection	Filtered Distribution	Unfiltered Distribution	Sold By	$/Ft or Each (1994)	Flow Rate GPM	Gal/Ft or Each
Rigid Pipe								
3/4" schedule 40 PVC			x		10, 20'	$0.17	12	0.025
1" schedule 40 PVC		x	x	x	10, 20'	$0.25	15	0.041
1 1/2" schedule 40 ABS	x			x	20'	$0.33		0.100
2" schedule 40 ABS	x			x	20'	$0.44		0.164
3" PVC leachline			x		10'	$0.35		0.385
4" PVC leachline			x	x	10'	$0.49		0.620
Flexible Tubing								
1/2" dripline			x		100, 500'	$0.09	4	0.013
3/4" dripline			x		100, 500'	$0.16	8	0.022
1" dripline			x	x	foot, 600'	$0.30	12	0.040
1" spa-flex[s4, s11]		x		x	foot, 50'	$0.65	15	0.041
1 1/2" spa-flex				x	foot, 50'	$0.95		0.100
3/4" garden hose			x	x	50', 75'	$0.58		0.025
Emitters								
Underground dripline			x		187.5'	$0.50	1.15	0.013
Standard infiltrator w/ 2 end plates			x		each	$50.00		76.000
Valves								
1 1/2" Jandy 3-way diverter valve	x	x	x	x	each	$27.00		
2" Jandy 3-way diverter valve[s3, s11]	x				each	$32.00		
Electric switch for 2" Jandy valve	x				each			
1/2" drip ball valve			x		each	$1.50		
3/4" PVC schedule 40 ball valve			x		each	$6.00		
1" PVC schedule 40 ball valve			x	x	each	$9.00		
1 1/2" PVC schedule 40 ball valve					each	$17.00		
2" PVC schedule 40 ball valve					each	$22.00		
1" PVC schedule 40 Swing check valve		x	x	x	each	$10.00		
3" ABS schedule 40 Backwater valve	x				each	$30.00		
Filters								
Pantyhose	x	x			pair	$2.00		4.0
Airless paint sprayer bag	x	x			each	$5.00		1.0
Pumps								
Little Giant 5msp (needs float switch)			x		each	$60.00	15	
Little Giant 5.5asp (integral switch)			x		each	$120.00	35	
Proven Pump B-1000 (needs float switch)			x	(x)	each	$100.00	17	
Little Giant 8E CIA RFS (integral switch)			x	(x)	each	$230.00	54	
Float switch					each	$30.00		
Double Ell (flow splitter) w/ access plug[s11]				x	each	$10.00		

3-way diverter valve

Double ell w/ access plug

Filtration

Filtration is the biggest problem in the systems which require it. Hair and bacterial slime are particularly difficult to handle. Three-foot-long hairs can work their way through a fine filter mesh then wrap around the pump rotor. Bacterial slime can grow on the downstream side of the filter, then slough off in large chunks.

Filtration is definitely an area for more research, but here are the options:

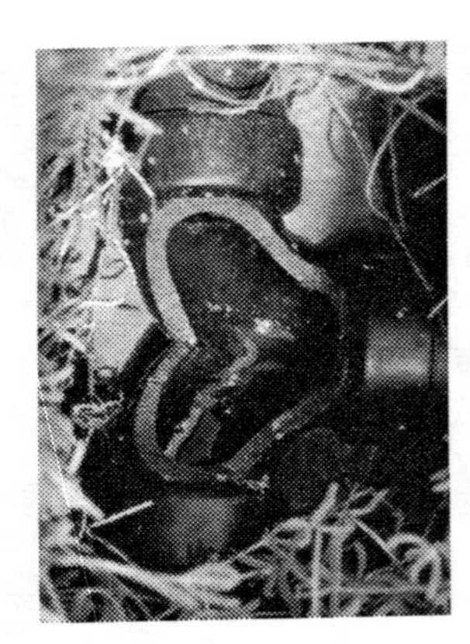

A cutaway view of a double ell, a flow-splitting fitting which appears to be self-cleaning with no filtration. This is part of the first branched drain network, which I tried valiantly to clog with pure kitchen sink water. I took the sink strainer out and pushed bowls of soggy granola and pot scrapings down the pipe for half a year. The p-trap clogged every other day, but the branched drain network never did.

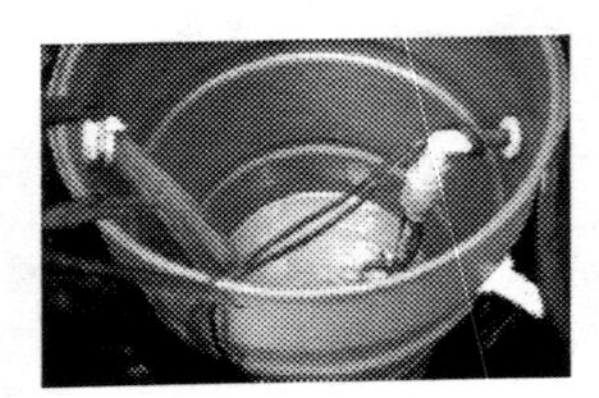

Net bag filter in a drum with pump.

No Filtration

Solids are easily handled by collection plumbing and are not a problem for soil—they're just compost. A system which doesn't have a pump or any holes smaller than 1" doesn't require filtration. Some expensive pumps can handle solids, but even these may have problems with hair. It is all but impossible to have automated, even distribution of greywater without filtration (except with a branched drain to mulch basins—see photo at right), but the absence of filter maintenance weighs heavily in the trade-off.

Net bag

The net bag is the most common greywater filter (see Figure 6, page 17; photo at left). It can be pantyhose or a fine mesh filter bag for airless paint sprayers (available in hardware stores). 75-micron mesh filter bags were used as pre-filtration in drip irrigation, but this technology has fallen into disfavor due excessive cleaning. Filter bags are disgusting to clean. Pantyhose are cheap enough to throw away rather than clean, especially if already used. They are also readily available and stretch to shed the bacterial slime that can clog a less-yielding filter.

Net bags are notorious for dumping gallons of backed-up crud irretrievably into the surge tank when removed for cleaning. A second filter on the outlet side is essential for systems with medium emitters; small orifice emitters would be a mistake.

Sand filter

Greywater to drip irrigation systems employ a sand filter that automatically back flushes itself, providing a high level of "hands-off" filtration. These can work well, but are expensive and require lots of electricity; they use 40 psi or so to push the water through the filter. A non-back flushing, unpressurized sand filter will clog quickly.

Septic tank

In a septic tank, water sits still long enough (at least 24 hours) for scum to float to the top and sludge to settle to the bottom, leaving smelly, infectious, but clear water in between. Most greywater systems avoid the worst odor and bacteria proliferation problems by distributing water as it's generated, eliminating settling as an option. If effluent is disposed of completely subsurface, this shouldn't matter. Perhaps the settling option will become more popular in the future, due to the infrequent maintenance it requires. Sludge can be pumped out of small settling tanks with a wet/dry vac.

Constructed wetland or infiltration bed as filter

Caution: Unproven designs.

A constructed wetland with successively smaller media in the direction of water flow (rocks to gravel) could be a good filter, if sized adequately for the influent. The same is supposedly true of an infiltration bed constructed on the same principle, if worms are present to prevent a slime mat from sealing the surface.

Surge capacity

Typically, surge tanks are located downstream of pressurized greywater sources and upstream of pumps, filters and small distribution orifices which slow the flow; anywhere surge capacity is needed to prevent a problematic backup. A bathtub can drain at 15 gallons per minute, far in excess of what a pump or filter can accommodate. For most homes 45 gallons of surge capacity is sufficient for a pump. If you habitually launder and run the dishwasher while you are in the shower and your kids are in the tub, you'll need more. The consequences of exceeding surge capacity have a major bearing on this decision. Temporarily slow drains are no big deal, but a washing machine pumping a load onto the floor is (see Table 5, page 34).

Surge capacity before the filter is given little thought in most designs and amounts to whatever space there is in the collection lines (see Table 3, page 29). This will determine how soon you notice slow draining and need to clean your filter. Ten gallons is a common amount; if you have short collection lines, you could install a prefilter surge tank if you have the fall to spare. This will need to be cleaned periodically.

TABLE 4: TYPICAL GREYWATER SURGES

Water Source	Typical Surge (gallons)	(cubic feet)
Washing machine	15 gal/1 min each cycle	2.0
Tub draining	45 gal/3 min	6.0
Low flow shower	20 gal/10 min	2.7
High flow shower	50 gal/10 min	6.7
Bathroom sink (low flow)	1.5 gal/1 min	0.2
Kitchen sink (one full basin)	4 gal/1 min	0.5

Surge capacity in distribution plumbing is rarely a limiting factor. It does, however, affect evenness of distribution. Suppose you have 62 gallons of surge capacity in 100' of 4" leachline and your pump cycles on with 8" of water in the tank and off at 3". The few gallons it pumps out with each cycle will only wet the first few feet of the line. If it were 100' of 1/2" drip line, the first gallon would fill it and the rest would be pumped out evenly over the whole line (although this is more work for the pump).

Orenco Systems[59] sells a manufactured dosing siphon which is reputed to work well.

To water with large, infrequent doses, improve distribution and give the soil some resting time, tether a mercury float switch on an 15" line, so the pump will not cycle on until the surge tank is nearly full. *Caution: Greywater can go septic if it sits in a dosing surge tank while you're on vacation. Also, long float switch lines can become tangled.*

FIGURE 20: DOSING SIPHON

Siphon spill point level should be between the top of the drum and the start of the curve on the inlet pipe (thanks to Eric Hughes of Berkeley for this suggestion).
Inlet (must be vented)
ABS Slip by 2" male pipe thread
Water Level rises in pipe as well...when the water level reaches the spill point and a large enough surge comes through to fill the full diameter of the pipe, a siphon will start and the whole drum will empty at once.
Water flows in a little at a time...
ABS Slip by female pipe thread
Outlet (must be unobstructed)
ABS Slip by male pipe thread
Ball Valve open to drain or clean surge tank

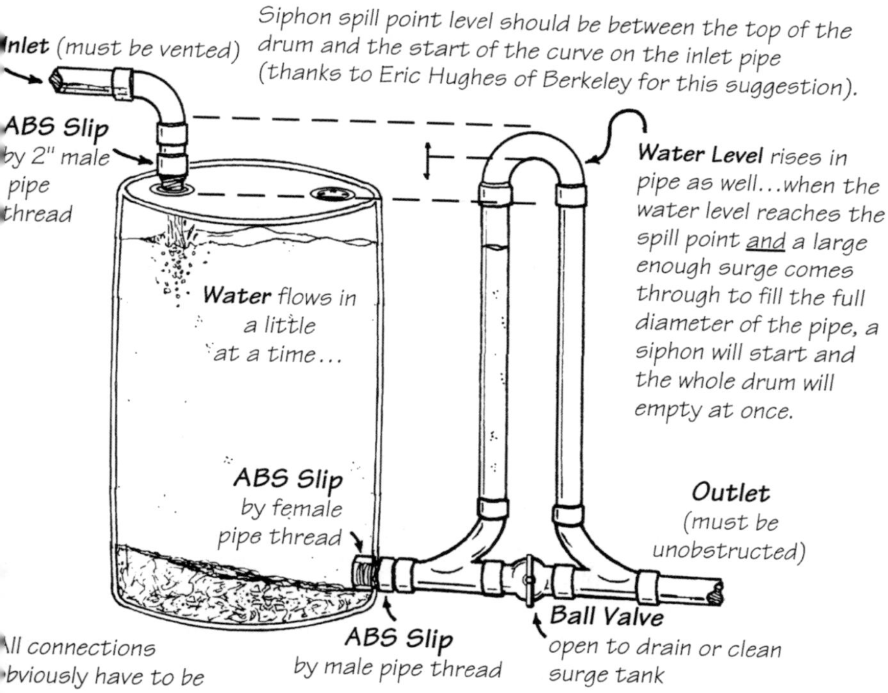

All connections obviously have to be watertight. The pressure on the drum must be low so it doesn't explode—just three feet of head puts over 3000 lbs of outward force on a 50 gallon drum..

A "dosing siphon" (Figure 20) is a way of turning many small doses of greywater into one large one, without the use of a pump. *Caution: It is tricky to get homemade dosing siphons to work reliably.*

If you try one, make sure the outlet line is small enough that an average surge can activate the siphon and not just dribble over the weir. Something between 1" and 1 1/2" should work. Sludge and scum both will accumulate and could eventually block the outlet.

Surge capacity in the landscape should be adequate to receive the largest expected surge. A few gallons of greywater on hard soil could run off into the street. A hundred gallons of greywater may not be able to fill a deep mulch basin around a large tree to the point where it surfaces above the mulch or runs over the basin, even if the soil is full of rain water.

Surge tanks

The simplest surge tank is a 30 to 55 gallon plastic drum. Various industries generate surplus drums that they will give away or sell cheaply. Empty plastic drums are UPS-able, increasing the practical scrounge range. Check out what was in the drum and reject any that held something toxic. Nurseries and hardware stores sometimes sell plastic drums. Greywater will corrode metal drums after a few years. Many people use inexpensive plastic trash barrels as surge tanks, but they become trash themselves in short order after they are weakened by sunlight and split by 300 lbs of water. Drums with tight-fitting, large lids are ideal, but much rarer than drums with two 2" bung holes. The latter will work if you don't need to put a pump inside, or you can saw the whole top off. Laundry sinks next to washers can be used as surge tanks (see page 15 for outlet installation).

Tank floating

Many surge tanks partially or totally buried during drought pop to the surface when heavy rains finally saturate the soil. If your design incorporates a buried tank, anchor it well against floating. The upward force on an empty drum surrounded by water is considerable; about 500 lbs for a 55 gallon drum.

Smells

Surge tanks often stink. The potency of the smell can be reduced by minimizing the amount of time greywater is held in the surge tank. Its noticeability can be minimized by sealing the tank and venting it through the roof.

Pumps

"Proven Pump" Model B-1000

Little Giant Model 5.5ASP

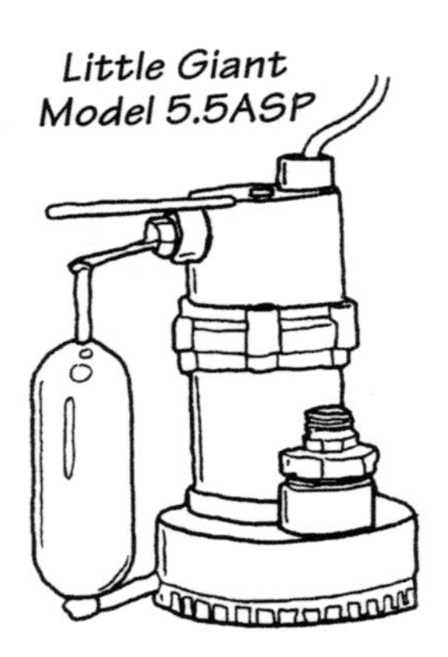

Little Giant Model 8E CIA RFS

I am no friend of pumps. You're better off not using a pump unless there is just no way around it. Systems that work by gravity are much simpler, cheaper and less failure prone. However, it is difficult to achieve even greywater distribution by gravity and, of course, impossible to water anything uphill of the greywater source.

Don't buy a pump unless it is rated to handle at least the lift and volume required for your system. It likely will be the most expensive part of the system. Don't, however, be tempted to buy a cheap pump; you will end up buying the good one anyway, after the cheap one fails.

Sump pumps are the most commonly used greywater pumps. They require a float switch to turn them on and off at the appropriate times. Many systems have a Little Giant Model 5 MSP pump, with a mercury float switch at the end of an electric cord. The disadvantage of this type of float switch is that it can hang up on the pump or the side of the tank and fail to turn on or, worse, fail to turn off. If not held in place by stiff outlet plumbing or some other means, the pump tends to migrate around the bottom of the drum as it's running, until if finds the spot where it can keep the float switch from shutting off. *Sump pumps require submersion for cooling,* so *operating them dry will fry them.* (They are relatively unaffected by running against a clogged distribution line, as long as they are submerged). One advantage of the mercury float switches is that the water level at which they turn on and off can be adjusted by tethering them at different heights with a length of cord. They can be used with any pump.

The Little Giant 5.5 ASP features an integral float switch that is relatively unlikely to hang up on anything. It turns on in 7" to 10" of water and shuts off in 2" to 4". This can lead to a small amount of water being pumped out frequently, which could mean that only the first plant or two gets watered. Overall, however, this is the inexpensive greywater pump of choice for most applications (see Table 3, page 29).

Besides being expensive and a maintenance hassle, pumps use electricity. In an average home, *a greywater pump can easily be in the top ten energy consuming appliances, accounting for 3% to 10% of total household consumption.* To maximize efficiency:

- Minimize the distance water drops in collection plumbing and surge tanks before reaching the pump. A wide, flat surge tank will waste half the fall of a tall, narrow one. Reducing the drop from, say, six feet to three may not be that hard and will significantly reduce electricity consumption.
- Likewise, don't pump water any higher than necessary. If you only have enough greywater to water half of your landscape, water the lower half.

Unlike water supply systems, with greywater it rarely makes sense to pump to an elevated tank and gravity feed from there.

- Use adequate-size distribution pipe to minimize friction loss. One inch pipe should be adequate for a pressurized greywater main for a home system.
- Size your distribution system for adequate flow, and don't pressurize your distribution plumbing any more than necessary. If your pump puts out 10 gallons per minute and the orifices in your distribution system all together can only handle 5 gpm, the pump will have to run twice as long as necessary. Likewise with pressure; more than 10 to 15 psi is not necessary for most distribution systems; a pump that maintains 30 psi in the system would be using two or three times the energy needed.

Valves

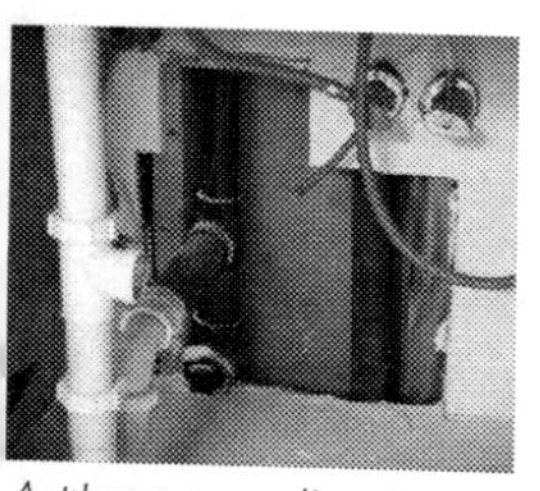

A three-way diverter valve is spliced in under a kitchen sink. Note that the incoming line from the kitchen sinks had to be raised to make space.

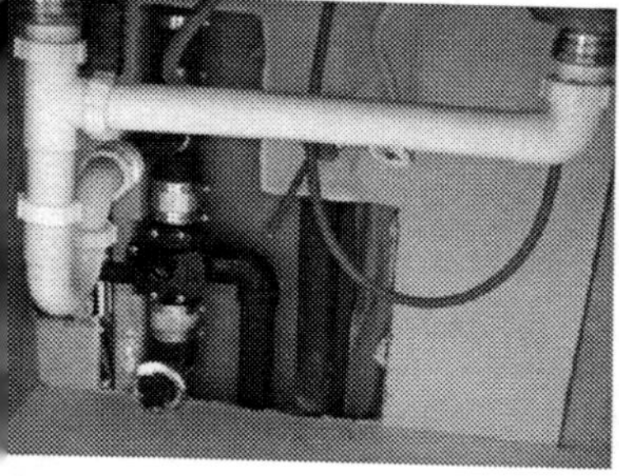

Valves are another expensive item on the parts bill, but they are critical so don't cut corners. *Gate valves* are less expensive than *ball valves*, but are far more likely to clog with hair or lint and fail to shut off completely. They are not recommended. Likewise, two ball valves are a less expensive way to accomplish the job of one *three-way diverter valve*,[s3] but if both ball valves are shut by mistake, an upstream pump can burn out, or water with nowhere to go may overflow. Also, if shut for some time, crud can settle in the water trapped above the valve, clogging the line. Diverter valves don't have these problems. While they are the best option, currently available diverter valves aren't nice and smooth inside, as they should be for wastewater. Anyone out there with a plastic molding factory?

Some diverter valves can be fitted with an extension handle so that a diverter valve installed under the house can be *turned from inside the house*. A motor drive is available for Jandy diverter valves so they can be turned from a remote location with the push of a button (as long as there is power anyway).

Check valves prevent water from uphill lines from running back into the surge tank and causing the pump to cycle endlessly. They also can be used to prevent blackwater from backing into a greywater line. Use *swing* check valves, not *spring* check valves. The latter clog too easily.

Ordinary electronic irrigation valves corrode quickly and lack adequate line pressure to work well in greywater distribution systems. Orenco Systems[s9] sells very expensive electronic valves designed for wastewater.

Designing for Easy System Maintenance and Troubleshooting

Greywater systems may require regular filter cleaning or other troubleshooting. *A well-designed system provides auditory and visual signs of its distress.* A system with an inaudible pump is much more likely to burn out when the pump strains unheard against a clogged distribution line. A system that overflows silently and cleanly into the sewer when the filter clogs will not be the most efficient. Weeks worth of greywater may be wasted each time the filter clogs, before it occurs to anyone to check it. Consult Table 5 on page 34 and design your system so it provides you with the proper cues—noticeable, but not catastrophic—when it needs attention. Always incorporate an easily switchable bypass to the regular drain for when your system needs maintenance or you don't want to use greywater. In addition to a manual bypass, you will want an overflow that splashes conspicuously but harmlessly outside if the system is non-operational (a more health department-proof option is an alarm that sounds when water overflows to the regular drain). Slow drains or water running loose in the yard are not catastrophic failures. Water overflowing into the house, greywater being siphoned into the potable water supply or a pump burning out are disasters. Table 5 (page 34) is geared to the "drum with pump," but can be applied with some allowances to most system types.

TABLE 5: FAILURE MODES
FOR "DRUM WITH PUMP" TYPE SYSTEMS

Failure mode	Design feature	What will happen
Primary filter clogging (before surge tank, occurs normally with use)	With no overflow	Drains will run slowly, then not at all, letting you know it's time to clean filter. *Note:* Disgusting water may back up into lower fixtures such as baths and showers.
	With overflow	Water will flow out overflow, letting you know it's time to clean filter, if you can hear it.
Secondary filter clogging (on the way out of surge tank)	With no pressure relief valve	Pump will work against clogged filter until you notice it or it dies. *Note:* Most submersible pumps can operate against a blocked line for a long time without damage, so long as they are submerged.
	With pressure relief valve	Water will be pumped out of pressure relief valve until you unclog filter.
Pump failure	N/A	Same as clogged primary filter, above.
Distribution lines or emitters blocked	N/A	Same as clogged secondary filter, above.
Check valve held open by hair	N/A	Water may leak downhill from distribution lines back into surge tank, causing pump to cycle on over and over.
Surge capacity before filter exceeded	With no collection line overflow	Drains slow, possibility of backing up into lower elevation fixtures, laundry overflowing at standpipe.
Surge capacity in tank exceeded	With no surge tank overflow	Drains slow, possibility of backing up into lower elevation fixtures.
Irrigation area saturated	No disposal alternative	Possibility of waterlogging, greywater runoff.

Cold Climates

A snowbound greywater greenhouse in Massachusetts filled with fresh veggies.

If you live someplace cold, all designs need to be evaluated in light of possible freezing. Knowledgeable local contractors can ensure that proper precautions are taken to prevent problems with the system. For example, all plumbing should either drain between uses, be below frost line in the soil, or be insulated. In remote applications where human contact is not a concern, it is not necessarily a problem if greywater freezes on the soil and accumulates; it will be treated when it thaws.[1]

The heat in fresh greywater, plus the microbial activity it fuels as it biodegrades, make freezing rare in distribution systems such as infiltration beds, box troughs and leaching chambers, even in very cold climates. Heaping leaves or other insulating material over the treatment area helps a great deal. To switch from a shallow, freezing-prone zone to a deeper, frost-free one, use a manual valve, or one of the automatic ones in Figure 21.

FIGURE 21: AUTOMATIC SWITCHES FROM SHALLOW TO FROST-FREE ZONES/LEVELS

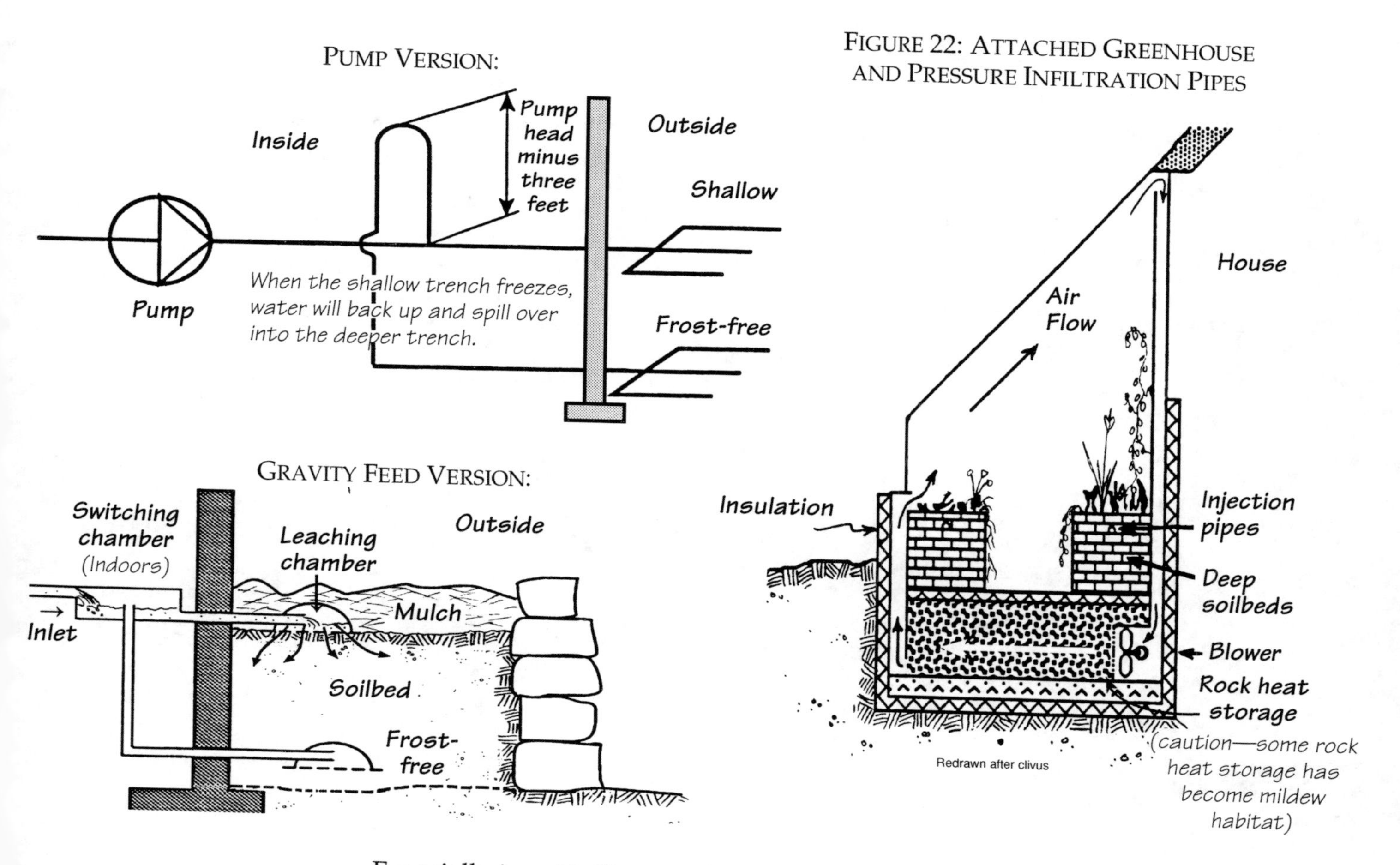

FIGURE 22: ATTACHED GREENHOUSE AND PRESSURE INFILTRATION PIPES

Especially in cold climates, the heat in greywater may be its most valuable attribute. To reclaim it, you can make or buy a heat exchanger,[8, s1] or just wait to drain the bathtub until the heat has escaped into the house.

Attached solar greywater greenhouses are the best option for year-round treatment. According to Carl Lindstrom, several greywater irrigated greenhouses in New England have been in operation since the 1970s. One 12' x 36' greenhouse uses a clear fish pool with a waterfall and biofilter plates on the bottom as the final treatment. Deep soilbeds store heat from the sun and from the greywater itself. This greenhouse was the highest cold weather producer of greens in the U.S. These soilbeds operate odorlessly and can provide salad greens throughout the long New England winter[s7, 9, 10] (photos page 22, 34).

Using Greywater During the Rainy Season

Is there any reason to use greywater for irrigation when it's pouring rain? It depends. If you live where irrigation is not needed but disposing of wastewater is difficult due, say, to low percolation, your greywater reuse may tend toward indoor cascading; using laundry rinse water for the next wash or using shower water to flush toilets[s16] (see *The Household Water Cascade*, page 39). In dry climates, all the reasons to use greywater still apply until the soil has absorbed all of the moisture it can hold, whether it's raining or not.

Even when plants' water needs are met by rain, on-site greywater treatment may still be ecologically preferable to municipal treatment. Sewage treatment plants consume energy and chemicals. The nutrient-laden water left over pollutes surface waters instead of returning nutrients to the soil and recharging groundwater. On the other hand, when soil is saturated, greywater can flow over the surface, posing a potential health hazard. If the soil remains saturated for more than a day, plant roots can suffocate.

During very heavy rainfall, runoff leaks into most sewage treatment systems and totally overwhelms their capacity. They release raw sewage into natural waters in these circumstances. People who don't know what to do with their greywater during heavy rain are in good company—the treatment plant doesn't know either.

A basin before being filled and concealed with mulch

If your greywater would otherwise go to a treatment plant, it is productive getting it into the ground almost no matter how wet it is. If you have the option of diverting greywater into a septic tank for the time when soil is saturated, this is ideal—the treatment level is good, nearly all of the water will be returned to the groundwater, and sewage plant loading will not be increased.

Topography & Mulch

However applied, soil and plants will purify greywater to a degree. Even wastewater flowing over the surface of the soil is purified to a surprisingly high level.[1] However, simple containment measures will assure a spectacularly high level of treatment. Contouring the ground helps contain runoff and concentrate irrigation water where it is needed, especially on slopes. Mulch basins and swales are also perfectly adapted for capturing rainwater and storing it in the soil. Put swales on slopes and basins by downspouts.

Basins

Basins consist of a hole scooped out of the earth and the tailings. Tailings can be piled downhill to make a basin on a slope. The walls of basins tend to get worn down, so they should be dug deep initially—10" at least—then filled with mulch. They should be sized to accommodate the surge volume they will receive, a bathtub full, for example. Most trees like to be on the edge of the basin or on an island in the middle. Plants that are resistant to waterlogging can inhabit the bottom.

Fertilizer is added over mulch to time-release to citrus tree watered through a branched drain network (note GW stream from outlet below rock at rear of dark circle).

Swales

Swales are long, thin basins (or blind-ended ditches) that run on contour, that is, on the same level across the slope. The downhill tailings make an ideal place to plant fruit trees. Roots can seek water in the bottom of the swale during drought and air in the top part of the swale during flood. As with basins, they should be filled with mulch.

Dry wells and auger holes

Dry wells are tall, narrow basins made with a post hole digger. They are particularly suited to tight locations, such as under a downspout between a house and walkway. Auger holes can be punched down through the soil with a 2" auger bit, available in lengths ranging from two to five feet. Auger holes amount to very little in terms of volume, but provide a proportionately large surface area for infiltration into lower layers of soil. These holes can completely change the infiltration characteristics of a soil underlaid by a thin hardpan. They also allow roots to reach reserves of water and nutrients they could not otherwise reach.

Mulch

Greywater coming out of a hose quickly vanishes under mulch and is contained by the basin. Mulching soil softens its surface and slows the flow of greywater over it, allowing greywater to infiltrate much more quickly. Mulch over greywater helps to prevent direct contact with it by kids and pets. Mulch basins are also a good way of reusing tree chips that might otherwise be landfilled.

Mulch slows the movement of runoff water, loosens the top layer of soil to make it more permeable, retards evaporation, helps lower pH and provides habitat for beneficial organisms. It absorbs water and supplies nutrients. Mulch reduces the loss of water through gopher hole sabotage of catchment walls. Spread mulch over all exposed soil in your yard and fill catchments to the level of the surrounding soil.

Mulch cautions: Dug-in mulch, which typically has a very high carbon/nitrogen ratio, can tie up nitrogen, starving plants. Avoid mulch from trees such as Eucalyptus in areas with new seedlings, as it contains substances that inhibit seed germination.

Plants

Types of plants

Using greywater on ornamentals that don't require acid conditions is safest, followed by fruit trees. As mentioned elsewhere (pages 4 and 8), greywater should not be used on vegetables or lawns.

ACID LOVING PLANTS (DIFFICULT TO KEEP HAPPY WITH GREYWATER)

Azaleas	Begonias	Bleeding Hearts (Dicentra)
Camellias	Ferns	Foxgloves
Gardenias	Hydrangeas	Impatiens
Oxalis (Wood Sorrel)	Philodendrons	Primroses
Rhododendrons	Zylosma	Violets

Irrigation needs

Treatment capacity is storage plus evapotranspiration plus percolation. This can be increased by deepening mulch basins and choosing plants with higher water uptake.

With few exceptions, the irrigation efficiency of greywater systems is low. With drip irrigation, a precise amount of water is delivered to the targeted area, in the correct amount at the correct time.[s2] Greywater, in contrast, comes out in random surges, in quantities that are fairly constant throughout the year. Eighty percent of the water from a well-designed drip irrigation system might be used by the plant, compared to 50% from most greywater systems. If you have a lot to irrigate and not much water, drip is the way to go. However, by applying the permaculture credo, "the problem is the solution," the unruly wetting pattern of greywater systems can be harnessed as a good complement to drip. Occasional large doses of greywater can encourage a fruit tree to send roots farther than little spots right under drip emitters. Eighty percent of the root mass of most plants is in the top foot or so of soil. A drip system will keep this area at optimal moisture to achieve optimal growth. But deep roots provide drought insurance and make use of stored rainwater. Instead of turning on the drip system occasionally for three times as long, application of a few hundred gallons of greywater for each mature tree can flush salts away from roots and encourage roots to go deep. Also, greywater can be directed to new plantings, so the entire drip system does not have to be turned on more frequently to meet the temporary extra needs of a few plants.

Effect of sodium containing (center) vs biocompatible (left) cleaners on tomato plants at high concentration. Control is at right. From a study I did at UC Berkeley.

Preserving Soil Quality

In arid lands, freshwater irrigation tends to raise the salinity and pH of the already too salty and alkaline soil. This simple, irresistible trend has been implicated in the collapse of all irrigation-based civilizations, including the impending collapse of the American West.[11] Unfortunately, greywater tends to do the same to an even greater degree, especially if sodium-containing cleaners are used. To minimize the damage, choose cleaners carefully.[s15] Rain (which has virtually no dissolved salts) is highly effective for flushing excess salts from the root zone. Just run rainwater from the roof into the mulch-filled basins which receive greywater. Give each basin several inches in a short period of time, then divert the rain water to the next basin. Mulch helps; see page 36. To remedy damage, add mulch, gypsum and/or elemental sulphur to lower pH. If pH is over 7.5, it will benefit from this treatment (a local nursery can supply materials and instructions).

Biocompatibility Chart

The chart below summarizes the biocompatibility of common wastewater constituents with the four most common disposal environments:

TABLE 6: BIOCOMPATIBILITY CHART

Material	Disposal Environment			
	Terrestrial		Aquatic	
	Arid Land Soil	Tropical and temperate soil	Ocean	Freshwater
Water	Highly beneficial	May be beneficial	No consequence	Little consequence
Organic Compounds	Beneficial food for soil microorganisms Fast biodegradation times desirable		Must be removed by oxidation in pretreatment to prevent depletion of oxygen dissolved in water Fast biodegradation times essential	
N Nitrogen	Extremely beneficial. N is beneficial plant growth's limiting nutrient	Beneficial. May leach into groundwater if added in excess	Probably OK. N is harmful algae growth's limiting nutrient but dilution makes measurable effect unlikely	Highly undesirable. N is algae growth's second most limiting nutrient
P Phosphorous	Beneficial. Leaching into ground or surface waters unlikely due low mobility in soil	Extremely beneficial. P is beneficial plant growth's limiting nutrient	Probably OK. P is harmful algae growth's second most limiting nutrient but dilution makes measurable effect unlikely	Extremely undesirable. P is algae growth's most limiting nutrient
K Potassium	Beneficial at washwater concentrations		Effect unlikely	
S Sulfur	Beneficial		No consequence	
Na Sodium	Highly undesirable. Toxic buildup likely	Undesirable but partly flushed from all but clay soils by rain	No consequence	Little consequence
	Directly toxic to plants, destructive to soil structure			
pH Acidity/ alkalinity	pH lowering desirable	pH raising desirable	No consequence	Little consequence
Cl Chlorine	Undesirable		No consequence	Little consequence
B Boron	Highly toxic to plants at washwater concentrations		No consequence	Undesirable
Pathogenic microorganisms	Harmlessly biodegrade under proper conditions		Diluted but could spread disease	Likely to spread disease
Industrial toxins	Disastrous		Highly undesirable. diluted but may bio-concentrate	Disastrous

Appendix B

Related Aspects of Sustainable Water Use

The Household Water Cascade

Ideally, water should cascade through the house and yard by gravity, from the highest vertical level and degree of purity to biological land treatment at the lowest level.[12] Every house could be surrounded with an oasis of biological productivity nourished by the flow of water and nutrients from the home.

Water is used for washing hands before it flushes the toilet in a common Japanese fixture

In the natural water cycle, water is purified in two ways: 1) distillation, where evaporation from the ocean leaves behind particles and dissolved salts; and 2) biological land treatment, where the action of microorganisms in topsoil biodegrades biological contaminants into nutrients, which are removed by plant roots before groundwater recharge.

Both natural distillation and biological land treatment of water compare favorably in effectiveness with artificial options such as activated sludge treatment. Conventional water use, by ignoring the structure and logic of the natural water cycle, encourages excess, depletes and contaminates aquifers, contaminates aquatic ecosystems, and bleeds the land of nutrients.

The healthiest relationship with the natural water cycle involves:

- Diverting a minimal amount of water.
- Diverting it just after it has been naturally purified so it requires little or no further treatment.
- Rigorously confining toxic materials that are incompatible with natural purification (such as motor oil and solvents) to their own industrial cycles.
- Adding to water only those cleaning products and other materials that biodegrade into plant nutrients or non-toxins.
- Adding these materials in an order that enables water to cascade through multiple household uses from those requiring the purest water to those tolerating the dirtiest.
- Distributing the nutrient laden final effluent to topsoil for on-site purification and reclamation of nutrients by biological land treatment.

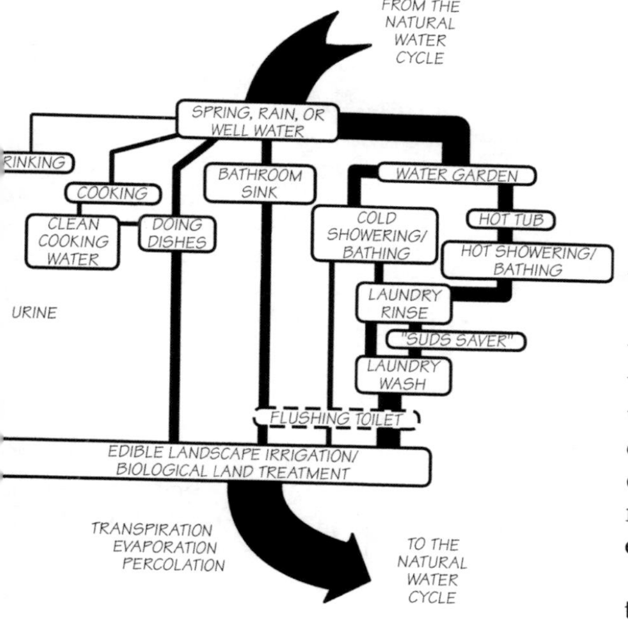

FIGURE 22: A HOUSEHOLD WATER CASCADE (THE WIDTH OF THE LINES CORRESPONDS APPROXIMATELY TO THE VOLUME OF WATER FLOWING THROUGH THAT PATH)

Water conservation measures are popular during a water shortage. However, in addition to conserving water, there are other reasons to cascade water and use it ultimately for irrigation—conserving dissolved nutrients, conserving the energy used to heat water, and reducing disposal problems. These other factors should be kept in mind when designing the water flow through a living environment in which water is plentiful.

Elevation relationships are a major consideration in the siting of different elements in the water cascade, such as water tanks, gardens, solar heaters, buildings, cooking areas, kitchen gardens, washing areas, bathing gardens and edible landscape features. In the home, drinking is the highest use, followed by cooking, bathing, hand washing, dish washing and clothes washing. Ecologically, it only makes sense to dump feces into water when dry feces disposal is infeasible. If so, this use comes last in the cascade.

If you're not going to build your own radical eco-home, cascading still can be employed in simple ways. For instance, water used to steam vegetables or boil pasta also can be substituted for some of the hot water used to do dishes. The water might be a little cloudy, but no more than it would be after you wash a few dishes in clean water. "Suds-saver" washing machines are a classic example of cascading; laundry rinse water is pumped to a sink or tank, then drawn back into the machine for use as wash water in the next load.

When showering in bathrooms with a shower/tub combination, save the shower water in the tub for hand washing clothes. The water will already be hot, so just add a little detergent. When finished, siphon the water outside.

Rain Water Harvesting

Even in dry climates, quite a bit of water just falls from the sky. More significant is its quality. Every other water source contains dissolved salts; greywater adds more. When irrigation water evaporates, this salt is left behind in ever increasing concentrations. Rain has virtually no dissolved salts and is highly effective for flushing excess salts from the root zone. Just run rainwater from the roof into the mulch-filled basins which receive greywater to flush them. Give each basin several inches in an hour, then divert the rain water to the next basin.

Rain water harvesting provides all domestic water by gravity for a house near Hilo, Hawaii

Our propensity is to seal the surface of the soil with pavement, roofing, plastic sheeting and compaction—efforts that transform our groundwater recharge zones into flash flood generation zones (Los Angeles supposedly absorbs only 10% of the water it used to). In arid lands, the best way to store water is in covered tanks or underground. Groundwater can be supplemented in wet decades and drawn upon in dry ones, a practice called "conjunctive use." To capture as much runoff as possible and get it to seep quickly into the ground, spread mulch, plant and shape the surface of the soil to make catchments in the form of basins and swales (see *Topography & Mulch*, page 36).

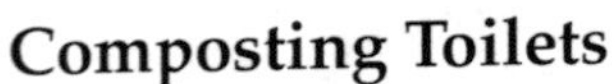

Composting Toilets

Used in conjunction with greywater systems, composting toilets promise a household that uses little water, recycles all of its nutrients and water, and employs no conventional treatment systems at all. Proceed with caution in pursuit of this lofty ideal; though some toilets have been functioning well for decades, we have collected mixed and contradictory reviews of composting toilet function. Carefully research your toilet decision.[s7, 13, s21] We are researching books on flush toilet alternatives and rainwater harvesting (see inside back cover)—please share your experiences.

Appendix C: Greywater Misinformation and common errors

If you focus on actual, whole life cycle performance, the prevailing beliefs about greywater system design crumble under the weight of the uncomfortable revelations below. Many players in the greywater field would just as soon not look in this can of worms. Pondering these failings has led our design path further and further from the mainstream of greywater thought—we're more realistic, so we hit the target more often. Our designs are holding up well in the field. In more than a dozen book revisions we've had to take back almost nothing we've said. However, when we looked at the results of our attempts to popularize good design it appears we haven't made much of a dent. The sorry state of average greywater systems is nearly the same as when we started in 1989:

- Most new greywater reuse systems are abandoned or achieve less than 10% reuse efficiency within five years.
- Many greywater systems consume so much energy and materials to save a little water that the Earth would be better off if the water were just wasted instead.
- The economic pay back time for the majority of complex (as opposed to simple) greywater systems is often longer than the system life.
- The huge majority of "successful" (i.e., give more than they take) greywater systems are so simple as to be beneath recognition by regulators, manufacturers, consultants and salespeople.

- Claims made for packaged systems are often greatly inflated. Some are very expensive and many don't work well.
- A web search on any variant of "greywater" will yield hundreds of sites, most of which could be used to illustrate the errors below. Many of these errors are recognizable from manuals of the early 70's, reprinted verbatim on the web as cutting edge, despite having been discredited in the field for twenty years!

The readers of our books do better than average, but we found they are still vulnerable to the siren song of greywater misinformation, the presentation of which is often authoritative and polished. So we now include a direct assault on greywater misinformation and common mistakes, in a two-pronged effort to get greywater systems to deliver more of their great promise.

We hope you benefit from the following survey of mistakes, which took many intelligent people many years to make and then recognize. This compendium of mistakes is constantly updated as a public service. That others may benefit from your perspectives and experience as well, please share them with us (especially if you've made a mistake which isn't in our collection) and we'll post them to our web page and include them in future book revisions.

Error-Out of context design

Wetlands in the desert. Irrigation of a swamp. Sand filtration, ozonation, and reuse for flushing toilets in a residence. Each of these are valid designs but applied in the wrong context. In a culture where standardized solutions are the norm from coast to coast, it is hard to remember the necessity of paying primary attention to the context, let alone know how to do it. Almost every time I say that something is so, the next breath is spent explaining why it is not so in slightly different conditions. I regularly have conversations where people repeatedly seize on a principle I've mentioned in one context, then vigorously misapply it to the next. As soon as I've explained the principle which overrides it in case two, they apply THAT to case three...this can go on for hours.

<u>Preferred practice</u>

The most general principle of greywater system design is that there are no general principles. All appropriate technologies are context specific (that is part of what makes them appropriate) however greywater reuse is EXTREMELY context specific. The final section on each of the common mistakes describes the inevitable exceptions when it isn't a mistake. Reuse or treatment, new construction or retrofit, soil and climate conditions, legal considerations; each of these variables in particular have the potential to change the design completely. Carefully check the list of greywater system design variables (page 8) and what to do about them in the balance of the greywater books. General background on context specific design can be found in our book *Design for Living with Nature* (see inside back cover) from which this summary is excerpted:

Context specific design

While there are no solutions which apply universally, there are a variety of approaches and patterns which can be applied to generate the optimum solution for any need in any context.

This is a vitally important principle of ecological design. In all cases the greatest efficiency—and quality as well—is achieved when the power of the tool is well matched to the task at hand. Frequent technological overkill is one of the saddest sources of waste in our society. Elimination of overkill does not involve real sacrifice. The resources saved by using simple tools for easy tasks can be applied towards performing more difficult tasks. Using transportation as an example, walking would be used for the tasks for which it is adequate, bicycles for distances too long to walk, busses and trains for distances too long to bike or in bad weather, planes for speed or great distances, and cars for special applications such as ambulances, mobile homes, or workshops. Getting superfluous cars off the road would enable the necessary ones to get around without being choked by traffic.

Cleverly matching the power of the tool to the task at hand is cheaper, healthier, has lower environmental impact and is more enjoyable—but ultimately more powerful than any single solution. Though uniform solutions appeal to centralized bureaucracies, attempting to implement a single solution across the board, without regard to context, will generate a host of new problems. Bare sufficiency produces optimal growth; deficiency is stunting, excess unbalancing.

Those readers who are used to single solutions will be quick to point out situations where, for example, a composting toilet is unsuitable. None of the solutions proposed here are applicable across the board, nor is it suggested that any of the technologies criticized here should be eliminated completely. What is suggested is that a range of solutions be matched to the range of contexts using common sense.

<u>Exceptions</u>

There are no exceptions to the "no general principles" rule.

Error-Overly complex, delicate and/or expensive systems with negative net benefit

As a class, these systems fail to refer to the big picture. A typical residential greywater system will save $5-$20 worth of freshwater a month, at best. This means that if the system costs more than a few hundred dollars, the owner would have been better off just paying for the extra water, and the Earth would have been less impacted by the wasted water than the wasted pumps, valves, piping, filters, and electricity used by the overbuilt system. It is this constraint more than any other which makes good greywater system design a real challenge. Complying with the "actual net benefit" requirement is so difficult in practice that it is very common for systems to just be built anyway, often with vague allusions to "demonstration project"...I feel this justification should be used sparingly, otherwise we will end up with lots of demonstrations of how yet more resources can be wasted.

In a residential context, any system which uses a pump,

This system spotted at the Los Angeles Eco Expo demonstrates a number of mistakes.

First, there's overkill. For several thousand dollars it does what a $400 "drum with pump" does. Second, the pictures on the poster board show filtered but unsterilized greywater coming out at high pressure through sprinklers and inundating a concrete walkway from both sides. That violates three health principles (at least it didn't show kids dashing through the sprinklers). The tank is also too big, so that violates a fourth...probably a record for one system.

filter or costs more than you spend on water in a year is suspect. Disinfection is extremely suspect. Systems which entail massive, permanent disturbance to the planted area, such as the state of California's mini-leachfield system, which involves burying truckloads of gravel in your garden, are also probably missing the point.

Unfortunately, strict interpretation of the requirements of greywater laws which are still works in progress tends to drastically reduce or completely destroy any possible economic benefits, in some cases without any benefit (except that reducing the proliferation of greywater systems was a perceived benefit to some of the major architects of the laws. See "Needed improvements to California's greywater law," in the Builder's Greywater Guide).

Preferred practice

Choose the SIMPLEST possible design, and BUILD IT AS WELL as you possibly can. Keep one eye on your original goals and the big picture throughout the process (see page 8). Keep asking yourself what the system is likely to look like in flood, drought, or in twenty years after three owners. What is most likely to have failed or been abandoned? How is the system likely to have been patched? Often the way systems get patched or modified later to comply with reality is the way they should be designed to be used in the first place. If no patch seems acceptable, there is a good chance the system should not be built that way at all.

Exceptions

When and wherever greywater is more valuable, the ground rules shift. Greywater skyrockets in value during drought emergency, and anywhere that other water sources are not available.

If greywater is the only way to save a $20,000 landscape during a drought, an expensive system that falls apart in a year may be justifiable. On the other hand, a very well-built, simple system which lasts for decades could possibly be made for the same price, if the design resources are available.

I designed a series of simple, very well-made greywater systems for a house where the only water supply is rainwater, stored for the eight month dry season in giant cisterns. The greywater system cost a few thousand dollars, but can provide the same amount of water as a cistern which would cost about ten thousand dollars. It also uses a fraction of the material and also solves the problem of disposing of the greywater.

Acute disposal problems can change the picture. I got a call from one Alaskan oil camp where the greywater from several hundred people was boiled down to ash, and the drums of ash shipped to the continental US for disposal (don't you love oil company engineers?) Compared to this, almost any system would be cheaper, simpler and more ecological.

A hotel in Big Sur was sending out their laundry at a cost of a few thousand dollars a month because they could not make a conventional on-site disposal system which could handle the water. A large, complicated, but well-built greywater system enabled them to do the laundry themselves, and they were able to pay off the investment in less than a year.

Sheer volume shifts the economics drastically. Almost any institution with several thousand gallons a day of greywater production and a like amount of irrigation demand would find that a complex system capable of treating the water so it could be distributed efficiently through irrigation hardware could be paid off in a few months to a few years.

US regulators are more comfortable with complex, expensive engineered systems than mysterious biological systems. It may be the case that an overly complex greywater system is the best alternative to an even more overbuilt conventional system, if that's all they'll let you do.

Error: Storage of greywater

Storage rapidly turns greywater into blackwater (see photo, page 4). The word "storage" should immediately sound an alarm, as should anything that includes a tank bigger than 55 gallons (for residential systems). If you doubt this, just fill a bucket with greywater and observe it as it progressively darkens and becomes more fetid. Bacteria multiply to blackwater levels as well, at least the indicator bacteria. In Mexico the *trampa de grasa* (grease trap) often included in greywater systems is a very popular way to commit this mistake-omitting or bypassing the *trampa de grasa* would be much better.

Preferred practice

24 hours is generally considered the prudent maximum time for storage. Since this is not enough time to, for example, store greywater from a time when irrigation is not needed to one in which it is, I find myself tuning designs to eliminate pooled greywater anywhere it occurs; just send it all straight to the soil. The fewer little anaerobic corners and pockets the better. My latest designs drain COMPLETELY…all the collection plumbing, distribution plumbing, and surge tanks (if any) slope at least 2% across their bottom surfaces.

Exceptions

Highly treated greywater (for example, after a septic tank and constructed wetland) can supposedly be stored for up to a month before it goes septic, depending on the BOD and temperature.

Surge tanks, which absorb peak flows (say from a bathtub and washing machine discharging simultaneously) then let them out immediately at a reasonable rate are OK.

Manually distributed greywater can be stored for the day to allow for manual distribution all in one session. Tanks for this purpose should be designed to drain COMPLETELY (not leave a bit of fetid greywater at the bottom to inoculate the next batch) and NOT BE TOO BIG as this invites misuse in the form of letting the water sit too long.

Greywater can be filtered effectively by settling in a septic tank. But then it must be disposed of like blackwater. In this case, the longer it sits in the septic tank the better (lower suspended solids and BOD).

Error: Cavalier disregard for legitimate public health concerns, and/or excessive paranoia about negligible health concerns

Some voices on the Web advocate growing lettuce and carrots with untreated greywater. Others fret about distributing greywater under nine inches of soil without disinfection. Some people worry about eating fruit which contains molecules from biodegraded dish soap, forgetting that they imbibe larger traces of dish soap directly with every glass of water and plate of food.

Preferred practice

Each user has to find their own comfort point on the paranoia vs recklessness continuum, and each community has to determine the outer limits of recklessness it will tolerate. Greywater reuse poses a very mild health threat in overdeveloped countries. Despite all sorts of grievous misuse (brought on in part by lack of useful regulatory guidance), there has not been a single documented case of greywater transmitted illness in the US. At the same time, it's definitely poor form to construct pathways for infecting people into your design, and totally unnecessary. Proper handling (using the same principles on page 4) can eliminate the health threat from greywater in third world countries.

Error: Treatment before irrigation

Plants and soil, especially the upper, most biologically active layer of soil, are fantastically effective for wastewater treatment. Pretreatment is often presented as an essential element in a greywater system, when in fact it may be more pointless than treating your wastewater before sending it down the sewer. Plants and soil are fine with funky, chunky water; it is pipes and people who may have a hard time with it. Pretreatment is only necessary to overcome limitations of the distribution plumbing to handle funky water. With a properly designed system, even straight kitchen sink water (very high suspended solids) can be reliably and safely distributed with no filtration whatsoever (photo, page 30).

Greywater "main" running down a Tijuana street—a bona fide health threat. In theory, this water could produce fruit and green relief in a sanitary way. Unfortunately, extremely high salt concentration from hand washing with small amounts of hand-carried water and generous amounts of "Fab one-Shot" from little day-glo packets renders this resource unusable; even though it is year-round water in a desert, not even weeds grow from it. A enlightened soap factory with a line of biocompatible cleaners and a suitable marketing plan could dramatically transform the colonia environment, exchanging fetid, mucky streets for thriving, shade and fruit-providing large trees.

Preferred practice

For simple residential systems, the preferred alternative to pretreatment is to 1) design the distribution system so it can handle funky water, in particular, high levels of suspended solids, and 2) design the distribution system so human (or animal) contact is unlikely to occur before the water has passed slowly through healthy topsoil (i.e., before it's purified).

The "Branched Drain to Mini-Leachfields" system I developed is an example of a system that fulfills these requirements in their most fanatically stringent interpretation; the smallest orifice in the system is an inch and a half, and there are no filters, pumps, valves or surge tanks to foul with solids. Distribution can be fully subsurface (see page 13 and pages 11-14 in the Builder's Greywater Guide).

These requirements can be fulfilled adequately by several other systems where greywater daylights for two inches before disappearing into mulch filled basins.

Exceptions

The systems described above are restricted to the use of large diameter, drain-type distribution plumbing, which is inherently less efficient than, say, drip irrigation plumbing. For small-scale systems, it is generally best to eat this efficiency loss, or go to a more labor-intensive, less sanitary system like bucketing.

For larger flows, say several hundred gallons a day or more, and a like amount of irrigation need, it can be very economical to pre-treat greywater to the point that it can be distributed by more or less standard irrigation hardware.

Error: Discharge of greywater directly into natural waters or hardscapes

You'd think this would be more rare, because it is so obviously wrong. They come in two categories; legacy systems, from places built 50 or 100 years ago before they knew any better and/or before it mattered, and new systems, which are generally more furtive and criminal-feeling, or just so unconscious it is beyond belief (photo below, page. 4).

Preferred practice

Almost anything would be preferred. Just dumping the water on the surface of the soil is a big improvement over dumping it in natural waters or impermeable surfaces. Dumping it into a mulch-filled basin would be a vast improvement.

Exceptions

Soapy creek from a legacy system at a hot springs resort constructed in pristine wilderness around the turn of the century.

When the receiving body of water has sufficient capacity to purify the water, and there is no other reasonable alternative. Sailboats on the open ocean are the only example which comes to mind. Even if you are in the middle of a vast wilderness next to a large river, you can just take a few steps back and rinse the shampoo onto soil, which will purify it before it goes into the river.

Error: Use of greywater for irrigating lawns

The only proven safe and reliable way of irrigating lawns with greywater is through underground drip tubing supplied by a backwashing sand filter type system; far beyond what most residences are likely to install. Unfortunately, turf accounts for the bulk of the irrigation need in the typical landscape, and lawn greywatering is by far the most prevalent violation of common sense greywater safety rules.

This is awkward to write. Do I criminalize thousands of greywater users who see no harm in what they are doing, or do I condone a marginal activity?

If the lawn receives traffic, by applying greywater to the surface you are short circuiting the all-important purification step (see health rules pages 4, 8), inviting direct contact with untreated greywater and the possibility of transmitting pathogens. The likelihood of transmitting disease is small (it would be laughed off in most developing countries) but it exists. The nightmare scenario: the day care center that "saves money and the environment" by irrigating the lawn with diaper wash water, which a dozen toddlers from other families then play in (I know you think I'm making this up, but I saw it at my daughter's very highly regarded day care; they were just trying to do the right thing and spaced out a bit about the context).

If the lawn doesn't receive traffic, then it is less risky to irrigate it with greywater but it shouldn't be a lawn in the first place; the only legitimate reason to have one of these resource hogs is that they are more fun to play on than say, a gravel and cactus garden. A better solution would to replace the untrafficked lawn with something else and irrigate that with greywater, if it needs irrigation at all.

Besides the health issue, greywatering a lawn is a pain in the rear. The system almost universally used is a hose from the washing machine or house plumbing which is moved around. Since the water has to be applied within the root system to benefit the plant, you have to move this hose to numerous locations in a very small grid, as compared to say, a large fruit tree, which would benefit from water left to dump anywhere within an area of hundreds of square feet.

Perforated pipe under a lawn will have efficiency in the single digits, and leave some areas completely dry.

Preferred practice

We suggest that you replace most of your turf with something else, replace what's left with a water-conserving grass such as Tall Fescue, watered with the freshwater you save from using greywater elsewhere, or just let your lawn go dormant when there's not enough rain to sustain it.

Exceptions

Lawns can be irrigated well and safely through subsurface drip ($1500 on up. 300 gpd greywater generation/irrigation need is the break even point where such a system starts to make sense).

Error: Use of greywater for irrigating vegetables

The primary reason not to use greywater on veggies is concern about transmitting disease (see page 4). Some people use greywater on veggies anyway. Why? See exceptions, below.

Preferred practice

If your goal is to just get rid of greywater responsibly and irrigation is not needed there is no reason to put it on food crops. If your goal is water reuse to lower overall water consumption, chances are that you will have more irrigation demand than you have greywater supply. In this case, use greywater first on ornamentals, then on fruit trees, and then use the fresh water you saved on veggies.

Exceptions

In the past I have categorically recommended against using greywater for irrigating vegetable gardens. As a certain fraction of greywater users have always and will always do it anyway, I've decided to illuminate the boundary between responsible resource reuse and reckless public health threat in this area. Also, after irrigating veggies with greywater myself, I understand the attraction better. We have a vast drip irrigation system, but it does not adapt well to irrigating veggies. The hardware is not that great; sprayers have very uneven coverage, they put the water on top of mulch instead of under, and you have to build the bed to match the spray pattern, except that wind blows this pattern completely off course. Lines with emitters in line are super expensive, and have clogged rapidly from filtered potable water. Additionally, I can't just hook up to one of the other irrigation zones; the veggies need about ten minutes every day, instead of, say an hour and a half three times a week. Also, during weeding, seeding, transplanting, growth and harvest the irrigation need varies tremendously. Veggies also are much more sensitive to daily (even hourly) changes in weather than fruit trees. They are a very poor fit to an automated system; I would probably have to settle for less than 30% irrigation efficiency, whereas I'm used to 80% for my fruit trees. Even if I wanted to pay for it, our small community water system doesn't really have this water to spare during the hot, dry summer months. Handwatering is the obvious alternative, and if I'm handwatering anyway, why not use hoses or buckets of free greywater, instead of fresh water which costs me nearly a penny a gallon? When hand watering with greywater I can get 80% irrigation efficiency, and am much more tuned into the plants.

A probable exception: Veggies irrigated subsurface with greywater in a greenhouse (photo p. 22 shows plumbing).

With the greywater systems I recommend there are several layers of protection, each capable of preventing the spread of infectious microorganisms on its own. When irrigating veggies with greywater the only possible protection is from 1) not happening to have anything nasty in the water, 2) not splashing greywater on the edible portions, 3) washing veggies, 4) cooking and 5), not getting sick even if you eat something nasty. Each of these offers tenuous protection. Additionally, greywatering vegetables is often manual, which inevitably results in some direct contact with greywater. If you're going to engage in this reckless practice, pay attention to what's happening with this slim margin of safety. If anyone in your household has an infectious disease, protection 1) is not operative and you should stop using greywater on veggies. For 2), exercise care in applying greywater, and give crops which are splashable and eaten raw a wide berth, even more so as harvest time approaches (e.g., carrots, salad greens). Always wash greywatered raw veggies with soap, iodine, or equivalent. Try not to splash too much, and wash your hands after greywatering (this extra wash water has to be considered in the irrigation efficiency for this system). As a last resort, hope for not getting sick even if you eat something nasty. I'm reluctant to mention this factor, but it seems to work in much of the Third World, where people catch plenty of nasty diseases but still not as much as you'd think.

Error: Distribution of greywater through perforated pipe or other system where you can't tell where the water is going

There are two problems with distribution of greywater through perforated pipe:

One, it will clog.

Why doesn't perforated pipe clog in septic tank leachfields? Because a septic tank is highly effective for removing suspended solids. Suspended solids are plentiful in greywater, even after the crude types of filtration sometimes attempted in home-brew systems, and these will eventually clog the pipe. If that doesn't clog it first, root infiltration will. If the pipe is big enough, and the greywater clean enough, it may take so long to clog that the durability is acceptable, but this is rare. A rarely used bathroom sink going into ten feet of four-inch pipe in gravely soil might last several years before failing. Laundry water will quickly clog almost any sized system.

Two, it is terribly unmanageable for irrigation.

Any system where you don't know where the water is going is all but unmanageable for irrigation. This is only a problem if you are trying to reuse the water, not if you are just trying to get rid of it. The problem with any system where there are emitters lined up in series (like holes in perforated pipe) is that the majority of the water will dump out the first few holes, or the lowest few holes, depending if the flow is low or high. Then these holes will clog, and the water will all go out the holes next door. In order to actualize irrigation water savings, you have to somehow coordinate with fresh water irrigation so that all the plants are getting watered enough but not too much. This is all but impossible to do with perforated pipe, which will invariably water one small area way too much the rest hardly at all, in a pattern which is constantly changing and invisible (if the pipe is buried) except in the form of distressed plants.

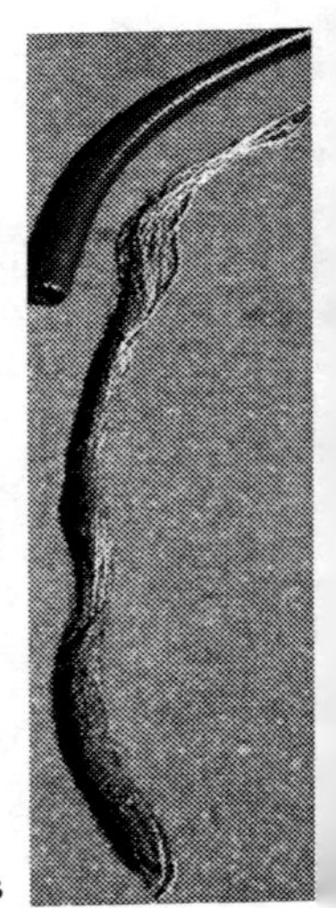

This 3' root plug was pulled out of a greywater hose which hadn't been moved for just six months.

You may be able to tune the pipe slope, hole spacing and size such that each hole spits out the same amount of water along the entire length of the system. This exercise has been performed by numerous greywater experimenters before you. However, this perfection is very fragile. If you alter the slope 1%, the flow a few percent, or if lint comes down and blocks some holes, the distribution evenness will all go to hell!

A series of garden beds with water flowing in gravel underneath is another example. Will the first bed get 90% of the water because the plants suck it up before it can move on, or the last bed, because it is low and the water rushes down to it? Who knows?

Preferred practice

If you must have perforated pipe, *add it as an extension to your septic tank leachfield and filter the greywater through the septic system so the pipe doesn't clog*. The preferred practice for separate disposal of residential greywater are mulch filled basins supplied by drain out back, or a branched drain network, with pipes a few inches above the mulch if allowed or in good sized underground chambers[s10] if subsurface discharge is required (page 13, pages 11-14 *Builder's Greywater Guide*). The preferred practice for reuse is to plumb in such a way that you know with some certainty where the water is going, so you can adjust your supplemental irrigation accordingly. This typically means a parallel system, or one with only one outlet. Examples are drain out back, movable drain out back, branched drain networks, well-made and regularly serviced distribution boxes, bucketing, etc. Crude but effective parallel splitting of greywater flows can be achieved by not combining the flows in the first place; each fixture has its own separate outlet. This is difficult to manage if the fixture use is highly variable and/or unknown, but works adequately in some applications.

For reuse of large flows, high level treatment and underground drip irrigation is preferred (pages 24, 8).

Exceptions

Effluent with suspended solids removed, for example, by a septic tank or sand-filtration, can be discharged through perforated pipe. For even irrigation, 1" pressurized perforated pipe lines with 1/16" holes on 1" centers up to 50' long have been used (photo, page 22).

Error-Fresh water designs & hardware used for greywater

Most people have more experience with fresh water than greywater. While it may seem natural to expect greywater to follow the same laws of physics, it doesn't. Here are some examples of the common pitfalls:

U-shaped pipe: Greywater should pass through a rigid "U" shaped pipe, seeking its level just like fresh water. Wrong! Crud in greywater will settle at the bottom of the U, clogging it. Preferred practice: 2% continuous slope in all rigid lines. This prevents airlocks as well, which plague inverted U pipes with low pressure fresh and greywater alike. Exceptions: 1) flexible lines won't develop this problem if moved once in a while, 2) pressurized greywater lines blast the crud through.

Cheap electric valves: Greywater distribution can be controlled elegantly and automatically using $12 drip irrigation electric valves. Wrong! Crud in greywater will prevent the valves from closing, greywater will corrode the valves in short order, and greywater rarely has enough pressure to make this type of valve work right even on the first day, as they are mostly powered by water pressure. Preferred practice: 1) forget automated valves, 2) buy super-expensive electric sewage valves.

Filters: This nifty sand/gravel/carbon/reverse osmosis/fill in the blank filter will filter my greywater just like it does my fresh water so I can...Wrong! Crud in greywater will clog that filter in the blink of an eye. Preferred practice/Exceptions: Check page 29 for greywater filtration options.

Soaker hose: I'll just run my greywater through these here soaker hoses...Wrong! soaker hoses are such a poor technology that they typically have 30% variation in flow when brand new and used with fresh water...and they soon clog with all but the cleanest FRESH WATER, let alone greywater.

Drip irrigation: See greywater to drip irrigation, below.

Error: Greywater to drip irrigation

Backyard tinkerers naturally tend to converge independently on the idea of running greywater through drip irrigation hardware to distribute it. There is no other way to achieve 80% irrigation efficiency, short of manually bucketing the water out plant by plant. The only problem is that it doesn't work. Of the hundreds of systems built during the recent (1990's) California drought, every one that I know of has been abandoned (see exceptions, below).

The most common configuration was a surge tank with an inlet filter and a float-actuated sump pump to pressurize the greywater lines. These systems work great for the first few weeks, then the filter clogs. At first, the drains are just slow. Then there is no denying it; it's time to clean that filter; the drains are not draining at all. When you remove the filter for cleaning (with rubber gloves, of course; a wise precaution), you realize the lines are full to the brim; fifty or a hundred feet of two-inch pipe's worth of chunky, days-old backed-up greywater comes out in a pressurized deluge into the surge tank. Fortunately, you are quick on your feet and you are only lightly spattered. Not more than a third of the solids caught in the filter have spilled into the surge tank. As you struggle to get your rubber gloves off so you can wipe the flecks off from around your lips and eyes, the sump pump cycles on. Horrified, you stand there paralyzed for a moment as the sump pump charges $300 worth of drip line with last week's split pea soup; by the time you wiggle under the crawl space and get the plug pulled on the pump, the drip line is history and the pump is stopped by hair anyway.

Preferred practice

Do something simpler and more robust with less efficiency, or go to a more labor-intensive, less sanitary system like bucketing.

Exceptions

AGWA systems, now out of business, made greywater to drip systems which were so well designed and built, out of such expensive components, that they actually worked. They cost a couple to several thousand dollars. This is not a home-brew-type system. Someone really ought to pick up this business where these folks left off. Update: Jade Mountain (see suppliers) is selling the "Earthstar," which may prove to be a good substitute for AGWA's m100 system.

Error: Automated reuse systems for flushing low use (e.g., residential) toilets

Automated systems for flushing toilets with greywater are complex and expensive. Flushing with untreated greywater will result in fouling of the tank and fetid anaerobic smells (see "Error: storage of greywater"). Treatment is fabulously expensive. The cost for a typical system touted on the web is $10,000. Even at the punitive water rate of $0.01 a gallon, that's 5 years of 325 flushes a day to recoup your investment, not counting lost interest, electricity, or system maintenance. The $650 Homestead Utilities system[s16], which is the cheapest I've heard of, would take 23 flushes a day—if you had a restaurant it could earn its keep.

Extreme economic infeasibility can indicate extreme ecological infeasibility; the earth could be way better off if you just wasted the water than if you wasted all the plumbing, pumps, tanks, filters and electricity needed to make this sort of system work.

Preferred practice

First, put in a low flush toilet (or a waterless composting toilet—see inside back cover). Then, "if it's yellow let it mellow, if it's brown flush it down." Third, toilets can be flushed with greywater by simply bucketing it from the bathtub/shower directly into the toilet bowl (not the tank, where it will fester). An added plus of reusing bathtub water in this way is that due to flush volume always being under direct intelligent control it is always less. Also, in cold climates you get a primitive but highly effective sort of greywater heat recovery as the bath water sits there and cools.

Once again, the Mexican housewife's system soundly outperforms the US engineer's system! If none of these preferred options appeal to you, you're probably better off just forgetting about flushing your toilets with greywater.

Exceptions

Multifamily, institutional or any other high use installations can benefit from flushing toilets with highly treated greywater, especially when incorporated in the original design of the building. If you have highly treated water already and don't know what to do with it, say from a constructed wetland, it may be worth supplying it to the toilet. An important advantage is that toilets need flushing every day, whereas irrigation need is usually seasonal.

"Clearwater" such as air-conditioner drip, reverse-osmosis water purifier reject water, and fixture warm up water is a natural for flushing toilets. It needs no treatment and can store indefinitely. Steven Coles of Phoenix, Arizona suggests that if you have an evaporative cooler, supply the toilet from its reservoir and you'll keep the mineral concentration in the cooler water from rising.

Error: Use of government agencies, trade organizations, engineering firms or salespeople for design of residential greywater systems

There is very little overlap between the set of practical greywater systems and the set of legal greywater systems. This would seriously hamper the government's ability to give out useful information, if they had it. Because greywater reuse is a new, marginal, rapidly evolving field, it is hard for ponderous bureaucracies to keep up with. The California greywater law and the pamphlet which explains it are especially misleading for hardware guidance-see error: using CA greywater law as example.

Also, there are few practical greywater systems which can be profitably installed professionally. It is likely that an established trade organization, engineer, or plumbing company would set you up with an unproven, overkill system adapted from some better known treatment technology. Therefore, you're pretty much on your own.

Appropriately designed greywater systems are not a very sales-friendly product; way too site-specific, variable, and inexpensive. The web features numerous generic, expensive, prepackaged greywater systems with fantastic claims, which seem to be better systems for the salesperson than the user.

Preferred practice

So far as I know our two books are the most complete and up to date references for home greywater systems. The designs in our books promise less than in other sources…because our books stick closer to reality. If the answer for your situation doesn't jump out of our books and web site, call us for a consultation.

Exceptions

For new construction sometimes an over-engineered greywater system is less over-engineered than conventional treatment. If the administrative authority requires it, gritting your teeth and paying up to ten times more for the false assurance of a brand-name product (which may never have seen success in the field but still seems safer somehow than you trying something on your own) may be the best option. Also, the prepackaged greywater system may actually be good, though the odds are against it and I know of none I can confidently recommend (please let me know if you make or have used a good one).

Error: CA greywater law held up as example to copy

California's new greywater law is an important step and certainly as well done as was politically possible. Too bad it's a step not quite in the right direction, as it is being emulated all over the US and the world. Some of the hardware recommendations are questionable. The mini-leachfield system, for example, is described in great detail as if it were a proven technology, but has been installed in no cases I know of and I can't think of any application for which I would recommend it.

Unrealistic laws have poor participation rates. Santa Barbara, for example, has issued approximately 10 permits for greywater systems between 1989 and 1998. There is evidence that during this time of severe drought over 50,000 Santa Barbarans used greywater! There are so many obviously overkill requirements that the entire law, including the sensible provisions, is dismissed as a source of design guidance.

Preferred practice

If you're a homeowner, don't follow the law unless you can get a favorable interpretation or have no choice.

If you are an inspector, sections of the law grant you nearly total discretion to approve whatever you want. Please exercise this discretion to discount the more pointless sections of the law and allow genuinely well-designed and executed systems (the sections which grant inspectors this discretion, the deficient sections of the law, and suggested revisions are all in the Builder's Greywater Guide, which includes the full text of the law with annotations).

If you are a regulator, don't blindly follow California or the UPC's lead when writing your own administrative authorities greywater regulations—instead follow Arizona.[2]

A reasonable regulatory stance leads to a greater compliance rate and a reduction in risk from the perpetuation of unregulated systems. Carefully check over and incorporate the list of needed improvements from the *Builder's Greywater Guide* and from our *Greywater Policy Center*.[2]

Greywater Systems and Suppliers

(References s1-)

Caution: Unless specifically noted, we don't know anything about the suppliers' experience or quality of their offerings. Suppliers change rapidly; this list was last updated June 2003.

[s1]**WaterFilm Energy Inc**, P.O. Box 128, Medford, NY 11763, Phone: 631-758-6271, Fax: 631-758-0438. Contact: Carmine Vasile, E-mail: gfx-ch@susn.com Web: endlesshower.com *Makers of a GW heat exchanger. It likes 24" fall to do its job, and works best with extensive shower use.*

[s2]**Geoflow**, 307-O West Tremont Ave., Charlotte, NC 28203. 800 828-3388, Fax: 704 347-0706. Contact: Karen Fergeson. *Their premium underground drip irrigation tubing is impregnated with herbicide to keep roots out and has a good reliability record.*

[s3]**Jandy Products**, P.O. Box 6000, Petaluma, CA 94955. 800 227-1442, 707 776-8200, Fax: 800 526-3928, 707 763-7785. E-mail: info@jandy.com Web: jandy.com *Makers of three-way diverter valves. You'll find these at pool and spa places easier than regular plumbing supply houses & plumbers.*

[s4]**Pacific Echo, Inc.**, 23540 Telo Avenue, Torrance, CA 90505. 310 539-1822, 800 421-5196, Fax: 310 539-5826. Web: pacificecho.com *Makers of flexible PVC. Call for local distributor.*

[s5]**Aqua-Flo Supply**, 30 S. La Patera Ln. Unit10, Goleta, CA 93117. 805 967-2374, Fax: 805 967-5509. *A storefront/UPS source for components.*

[s6]**ReWater Systems**, 477 Marina Parkway, Chula Vista, CA 91910. 619 585-1196, Fax: 619 585-1919. Contact: Steve Bilson. Web: www.rewater.com *Maker of plastic distribution cones and a range of GW systems from $1295 and up. Active in GW politics.*

[s7]**Clivus Multrum Inc.**, 15 Union St., Lawrence, MA 01840. 800 4-CLIVUS (800 425-4887), 978 725-5591, Fax: 978 557-9658. *Longtime manufacturer and distributor of composting toilets. Supplier of GW systems and information. Infiltration bed, greenhouse and freeze switch designs are courtesy of Carl Lindstrom.*

[s8]**NutriCycle Systems (Formerly Hanson Associates)**, 3205 Poffenberger Rd., Jefferson, MD 21755. 301 371-9172. Contact: John Hanson, E-mail: jhanson@nutricyclesystems.com Web: nutricyclesystems.com *"Nutrient recycling system" composting toilet, box trough GW systems. Leaching chamber and box trough designs are thanks to John Hanson.*

[s9]**Orenco Systems**, 814 Airway Avenue, Sutherlin, OR 97479-9012. 800 348-9843, 541 459-4449, Fax: 541 459-2884. Web: orenco.com *Established makers of sand filter septic systems, components, seminars.*

[s10]**Infiltrator Systems**, Web: infiltratorsystems.com, 800 221-4436. *Plastic "infiltrator" gravel-less infiltration chambers of good quality.*

[s11]**Jade Mountain Inc/Real Goods**, 360 Interlocken Blvd., Broomfield, CO 80021. 800 442-1972 orders, Fax: 303 222-3599, Web: realgoods.com/renew, E-mail: info@jademountain.com *Mail order source for spa-flex, three-way diverter valves, GW systems and parts.*

[14]**Tad Montgomery & Associates**, P.O. Box C-3, Montague, MA 01351. 413 367-0068. E mail: tad@shaysnet.com *Ecological Engineering, constructed wetlands, composting toilets, etc.*

[15]**Oasis Biocompatible Cleaners**, dist. by Bio Pac, Inc., 584 Pinto Court, Incline Village, NV 89451. 800 225-2855, Fax: 209 844-2134. Contact: Collin Harris. Web: bio-pac.com, E-mail: info@bio-pac.com

[16]**Homestead Utilities**, 17366 E. Meadow Lane, Mayer, AZ 86333-4119. 800 CYCLE-H2O. Contact: Anton. E-mail: theo@leque.com Web: leque.com *According to their literature, make $556 system that filters and chlorinates greywater to reuse for flushing toilets.*

[8]**Northwest Water Source (formerly Greywater Management)**, P.O. Box 2766, Friday Harbor, WA 98250. 360 378-8900, Fax: 360 378-8790 Contact: Tim Pope, E-mail: water@waterstore.com. *"Aquabank" auto-backwashing sand filter and ozone/UV disinfection system. Alternative water sourcing, rainfall catchment.*

Natural Systems, 811 St. Michaels Dr., Ste. 102, Santa Fe, NM 87505. 505 988-7453. Fax: 988-3720 E mail: nsi@natsys-inc.com Website: natsys-inc.com Contact: Micheal Odgen. *One of the first engineering firms specializing in constructed wetlands—a good outfit.*

North American Salt Co., 877 IMC-SALT, Fax: 877 423-7258. Contact: Jerry Poe, 913 344-9195, Fax: 913-338-7924, E-mail: poe@imcsalt.com Web: www.nasalt.com *Manufacturer & distributor of potassium chloride softener salt.*

Enviro Options (PTY) LTD, P.O. Box 13, Kya Sands, South Africa, 2163. 27 11 708-2245, Fax: 27 11 708-2180. Contact: Walter, E-mail: walter@eloo.co.za Website: www.eloo.co.za *"Enviro Loo" best composting toilets in the world, according to one source.*

Further Reading and Resources

(References 1-)

[1]**Green Land—Clean Streams: the Beneficial Use of Waste Water Through Land Treatment** Center for the Study of Federalism. 1972. Center for the Study of Federalism, Temple University, Philadelphia, PA. *Analysis of large scale land treatment facilities. Currently out of print, but photocopies are available. Summary table of treatment effectiveness, which is amazingly high, even for overland flow.*

[2]**Greywater Policy Center**, Web: oasisdesign.net/greywater/law *Includes California, Arizona, New Mexico and other laws.*

[3]**Greywater Pilot Project Final Report** Los Angeles Department of Water Reclamation. 1992. *Report on first quantitative field testing of greywater health safety. May be available from Los Angeles Department of Water and Power, P.O. Box 1111, Room 1315, Los Angeles, CA 90051-0100. 213 367-4141, Fax: 213 367-0907.* E-mail: victoria.cross@water.ladwp.com

[4]**Excreta Disposal for Rural Areas and Small Communities** Wagner, E. and J. Laniox. 1958 (reprinted 1971). Monograph #39, World Health Organization, Geneva, Switzerland. *Information and diagrams about the effectiveness of soils for containing and processing nutrient and pathogen contamination from human feces, as well as other technologies.*

[5]**Design for Living with Nature** Art Ludwig. *An overview of natural economics, architecture and landscaping, including "landscape direct" designs for greywater use* (see inside back cover).

[6]**Design Manual; Constructed Wetlands for Municipal Wastewater Treatment** U.S. Environmental Protection Agency, Office of Research and Development. 1988. Center for Environmental Research Information, Cincinnati, OH 45268.

[7]**"Cleaners for Greywater Systems"** Office of Aridland Studies, University of Arizona, Office of Aridland Studies, University of Arizona, Tucson, AZ 85719. 602 621-1955, Fax: 621-3816. Contact: Martin Karpiscak. *Independent lab assessment of cleaners for greywater, general principles and lab results only, no interpretation.*

[8]**"Greywater Heat Recovery"** available from NATAS (National Appropriate Technology Assistance Service), P.O. Box 2525, Butte, MT 59702. 1-800-428-2525.

[9]**"Using Greywater"** Carl Lindstrom, Clivus Multrum Inc (see s7)

[10]**"Greywater for the Greenhouse"** Rockefeller A.A., [1978] and The Greenhouse as Leachfield. The National Sanitation Foundation, Ann Arbor, MI [1978]; Clivus Multrum Inc. [1979].

[11]**Cadillac Desert** Mark Reisner, 1986. Viking Penguin Inc., New York, NY *Exceedingly well researched history of western water.*

[12]**Residential Water Reuse** Milne, Murray. 1979. California Water Resources Center, University of California at Davis, report #46. Regents of the University of California. *550 page, highly readable gold mine of fascinating information and history of water reuse. 50 page annotated bibliography. Out of print but available from NTIS 5285 Port Royal Rd., Springfield, VA 22161.*

[13]**Composting Toilet System Book** David Del Porto, Carol Steinfeld. CEPP, 1999. *Tons of raw information on composting toilets.*

The Toilet Papers; Recycling Waste and Conserving Water Sim Van Der Ryn Available from Chelsea Green, 800 639-4099

[14]**Builder's Greywater Guide** Art Ludwig. *See inside back cover.*

[15]**Monitoring Graywater Use: Three Case Studies in California** Available from California DWR, Arturo Carvajal 916 327-1622

[16]**Branched Drain Greywater Systems** Art Ludwig. *See inside back cover.*

Additional Reading and Resources

National Small Flows Clearinghouse West Virginia University, P.O. Box 6064, Morgantown, WV 26506-6064. 800 624-8301. *Clearinghouse with a wealth of information on water treatment.*

The Septic System Owner's Manual. Lloyd Kahn, Blair Allen, & Julie Jones. Shelter Publications 2000. 800-307-0131 Web: shelterpub.com *Everything you need to know about maintaining a septic system. Includes section on alternative systems.*

Designing and Maintaining Your Edible Landscape Naturally Robert Kourik. 1986. Metamorphic Press, P.O. Box 1841, Santa Rosa, CA 95402. *Landmark reference work on edible landscaping. A phenomenal quantity of quality information.*

Basic Plumbing Illustrated Editors of Sunset Magazine. Sunset Books, Lane Publishing, Menlo Park 1983. *Basic plumbing reference.*

On-Site Stormwater Management: Applications for Landscape and Engineering Ferguson, Bruce K., Thomas N. Debo. 2nd Edition, Van Nostrand Reinhold 1989.

Rainwater Harvesting; The Collection of Rainfall and Runoff in Rural Areas Arnold Pacey. Intermediate Technology Publications, London 1986. *Great resource for residential and agricultural rainwater harvesting in third world conditions.*

A Cycle of Cycles-A Guide to Wastewater Recycling in Tropical Regions Katja Hansen & Douglas Mulhall. European Commission Directorate General 1-B, 1998. *Economic, social and technical guide to tropical and Mediterranean wastewater recycling for flows from less than 50,000 inhabitants, with special reference to agriculture.*

The Chemical, Physical and Microbiological Characteristics of Typical Bath and Laundry Waste Waters Hypes, W.D. Batten, L.E., NAS

"Assessment of On-Site Graywater and Combined Wastewater Treatment and recycling Systems" *Available from: National Association of Plumbing-Heating-Cooling Contractors, 180 S. Washington St., P.O. Box 6808 Falls Church, VA 22046, 1-800-533-7694 Website: phccweb.org*

"A Homeowner's Guide to the Safe Use of Greywater During A Drought" Kenneth W. Kizer, M.D., M.P.H. (Director, California Department of Health Services). March 1991. State of California Department of Health Services, Environmental Management Branch. *Call the greywater hotline, (916) 323-1675 for a free copy. Surprisingly liberal, common sense guidelines for the safe use of GW.*

Australian Resources & Suppliers

Domestic Greywater Reuse: Overseas Practice and its applicability to Australia Barry Jeppesen and David Solley, Brisbane City Council. Research Report No. 73, March 1994. Urban Water Research Association of Australia, c/o Water Services Association of Australia, P.O. Box 13172, Law Courts Post Office, Melbourne 8010, Ph: 61 3 96060678 http://www.wsaa.asn.au *The most substantive report on greywater in Australia. A wealth of information of interest to regulators wondering what to do about greywater in their jurisdiction, including: detailed information on water use, greywater sources and quality, microbiological and chemical properties of greywater, soil considerations, irrigation needs, possible effects of widespread greywater use on public works, and design considerations. There is relatively little here for the individual or contractor.*

Australian Water and Wastewater Association, P.O. Box 388, Artarmon, NSW 2064, phone 61 2 413 1288, fax 413 1047 web http://www.awwa.asn.au. *Australian member of an international network of organizations which collect and disseminate information on water and wastewater. Contact: Brian McRae.*

Tagari Publications, Permaculture Institute, P.O. Box 1, Tyalgum, NSW 2484. Phone 02 66 79 34 42, fax 02 66 793-567. *Publisher of a series of books on "permaculture," a system of ecological development which includes greywater reuse along with many other good ideas.*

Environment Equipment Pty Ltd 41A Jarrah Drive Braeside, VIC 3195 Ph:61 3 9587 2447 Fax: 61 3 9587 5622 Web:.rotaloo.com Contact: Buzz Burrows. *Designers of composting toilets and three greywater system designs all approved by the Australian EPA, the latest Electropure system treating the water from 10 houses and recycling it for above ground irrigation.*

Aquasaver (Australian brand), Sweetglen Pty Ltd, c/o Glen Gaskon, 26 Wunnulla Street, Thornside, QLD. Ph (07) 2075137. *The "Aquasaver" aspires to be a fully self-contained greywater system that is designed to collect and reuse all of the household's greywater. The system incorporates a fiberglass container, filters with an automatic backwash to sewer, option to disinfect, electronically operated valves and effluent pumps. Still in development. Estimated cost $1500.*

Clivus Roughing Filter, Clivus Multrum, P.O. Box 126, Strathpine Queensland 4500. Phone: 61 07 3889 6144. *Removes grease, hair, food, lint and other matter etc. from the total household greywater flow allowing it to be diverted for reuse/recycling. Clivus also markets a stretch filter greywater system. Estimated cost $550.*

Deks Water Saver, Deks Industries Pty Ltd, c/o P.O. Box 569, Bayswater Victoria 3153. *The Deks Water Saver is a soft rubber funnel that can be inserted into the inspection opening of an existing waste pipe. When connected to a hose the fitting diverts the greywater for garden use. Estimated cost. $10.*

Sullage Diversion Valve, Canmas partners, c/o Daniel Cantore Ph 61 7 3206 7411, Redlands Shire, QLD. *The diversion valve is a simple pvc device that can be installed beneath some existing fixture, such as a laundry tub, to allow manual diversion of flow for reuse/recycling. Estimated cost. Less than $100.*

Eco Design Sustainable Housing. P.O.Box 2000, Fairfield Gardens 4103, Australia Ph 61-7-3342-4497, Fax - 61-7-3342-4496 Web: www.greywater.com.au E mail: information@greywater.com.au *Greywater irrigation systems and composting toilet design manual $45.00 US (for orders outside Australia) or $65.00 AUD (within Australia)*

Greywater systems & composting toilets Mark The Spark, P.O .Box 37, Snug, Tasmania, Australia, 7054. Phone: (03) 6267 4141, FAX : (03) 6267 4591 E mail: markthespark@tassie.net.au

Index/Glossary

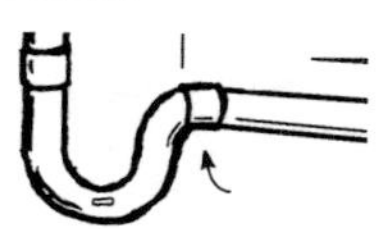

R

S

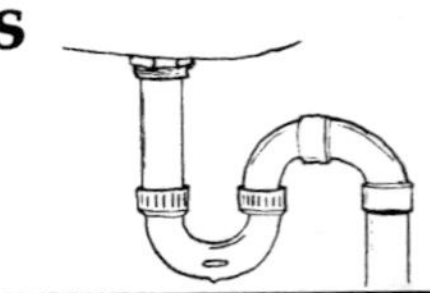

T

U

V

W